MW00627782

"A must-read for anyone who wisl
bonization strategy."

— AL HUEHN
President and CEO, Topco Oilsite Products

"Finally! A pragmatic road map for oil and gas companies that want to successfully evolve into the next-generation energy ecosystem. This book also provides a guide for environmental NGOs, legislators, regulators, and people in the general business community who want to partner with oil and gas companies on creating wise, stable policies and incentives to move society toward a lower-carbon future."

— GEORGE SPARKS
President and CEO, Denver Museum of Nature & Science

"U.S. oil and natural gas companies are vital to a low-carbon future, and Tisha provides must-read insights into how companies can activate their lower-carbon ambitions."

— ANNE BRADBURY
CEO, American Exploration & Production Council

"Tisha gracefully compiles many industry perspectives into a one-of-a-kind guide to charting your role in the low-carbon future. A great read for leaders ready to act."

— ANTHONY ONI
Managing Partner and CEO, Elevate Future Fund

"Realizing decarbonization and ESG commitments begins with the ability to quantify baseline emissions, from a range of sources. With *Real Decarbonization*, Tisha has done the legwork to define a pathway for the energy transition. *Real Decarbonization* provides a practical leadership road map to achieving net-zero targets."

— DAN HARPLE
Founder and CEO, Context Labs

"The energy transition is going to be a multi-decade, multi-trillion-dollar investment opportunity. The oil and gas industry is uniquely positioned to lead the transition to a lower-emissions future with its deep expertise and assets in the existing energy system. Tisha Schuller's expert insight in this most recent book charts out a map and a pathway to not just get there, but win at it."

— KEVIN KRAUSERT
CEO and Co-Founder, Avatar Innovations

"Despite our progress, 80 percent of the world's energy still comes from unabated fossil fuels, and the transition to non-carbon-emitting energy sources will be a long and winding road. What is the role of current oil and gas companies in the transition? What can they do to mitigate their climate impact along the way? Tisha Schuller's book provides a comprehensive guide for any company looking to seriously address those questions and serves as a reminder that any company ignoring them is courting irrelevance."

— ARMOND COHEN
President and Co-Founder, Clean Air Task Force

"Through *Real Decarbonization*, Tisha has invited you to a private dinner party with some of industry's most forward-thinking leaders in the energy transition. It's personal, insightful, and gives great context to the challenges and opportunities leaders face."

— MATT KOLESAR
Chief Environmental Scientist, ExxonMobil

"Transforming today's energy systems to deliver low-carbon and low-cost solutions requires that we embrace disruptive innovation and act deliberately. Tisha Schuller once again provides us with a clear-eyed, pragmatic, and detailed guide to operationalize our collective ambition."

— PAULA GANT
President and CEO, GTI Energy

"*Real Decarbonization* captures the essence and opportunity in front of our industry. Tisha takes a pragmatic look at the opportunities that exist today, even as we look toward the solutions needed for tomorrow. Simply put, it's *the* discussion to have right now in your organization at such an important time in our industry."

— PIERCE H. NORTON II
President and CEO, ONEOK

"The world is demanding cheaper, more reliable, cleaner energy — and lots of it. While developed nations are seeking elegant zero-carbon energy solutions, undeveloped nations are scrambling for any energy solution, no matter how crude, to bring billions out of energy poverty. The world has yet to deliver a truly sustainable energy solution that can carry the weight of the world. But that is about to change — America's oil and gas workforce has awakened to the opportunity in front of them. Seasoned with wisdom from leaders in the arena, Tisha's book provides an excellent blueprint to get our proven energy professionals off the bench and in the game."

— TOBY RICE
President and CEO, EQT Corporation

"The adoption of new technologies to mitigate climate change will be a gradual process, and in the meantime, humanity will undoubtedly continue to use fossil fuels. It is therefore essential that oil and gas companies decarbonize their product value chains in the near term. Many companies now have decarbonization targets in place, and this book is a must-read for any oil and gas executive looking to translate those targets to specific and focused operations that will achieve meaningful emissions reductions."

— NAOMI L. BONESS
Managing Director, Stanford Natural Gas Initiative
Co-Managing Director, Stanford Hydrogen Initiative

"Successful energy leaders will approach decarbonization with curiosity, with a microscope and a telescope simultaneously. They'll be in the details while also stepping back, seeing the big picture, and looking forward to the future. Tisha helps leaders think intentionally about reframing the game."

— SUZANNE OGLE
President and CEO, Southern Gas Association

REAL
DECARBONIZATION

REAL
DECARBONIZATION

How Oil and Gas Companies Are
Seizing the Low-Carbon Future

TISHA SCHULLER

Lodgepole Pine
PUBLISHING

ISBN: 978-0-9993220-1-7

For Carter, Alec, Megan, Ethan, Matthew,
Drew, Nicolas, Sophia, Willow, Billie Lou,
Levi, Lake, and Lachlan.

After all, we are embarking on real
decarbonization for all of you.

May we be worthy of your futures.

TABLE OF CONTENTS

CHAPTER 1

You Don't Have to Like This Book to Use This Book

"We want to solve the world's greatest problems. We think our company can contribute to that."

— Chad Zamarin, Williams Companies

You don't have to like this book.

But you need a real decarbonization strategy regardless of how you feel about the energy transition.

Helping you to develop your strategy — based on guidance from some of boldest leaders in oil and gas, who are implementing their own — is the reason I've written this book.

And make no mistake: I have written this book for everyone in our sector, believers and skeptics alike. For both, the pressures to change and the through line of change will be the same. And if you're an inside-industry skeptic, your skepticism does not hold a candle to the skepticism of those outside of oil and gas! More on that in a moment.

Energy transition enthusiasts: You are mission-critical to seizing this opportunity. You already know what I learned from interviewing 20 leaders, both within and adjacent to our industry, for this book: that oil and gas workforces are excited and inspired by our companies' efforts in leading energy transition innovation. All generations exude this enthusiasm, but millennial employees (the largest generational segment of our workforce) are exceptionally fervent. Company employees consistently conveyed to the leaders I interviewed a sense of responsibility for addressing climate change; this responsibility has translated into a passionate desire to contribute to accelerating the energy transition.

And yet our workforce, like the public, does have a significant number of energy transition skeptics. These skeptics are not "science deniers" nor any other demeaning stereotype. Inside-industry energy transition skeptics have good reason to raise concerns over company environmental, social, and governance (ESG) and decarbonization commitments and plans.

Skeptics: You are also mission-critical. Your often staunch opposition is grounded in physics, values, geopolitics, history, economics, and reality. In many ways that deeply matter, you are right. (More on that, too, in a bit.) Throughout my interviews, oil and gas company leaders talked about the imperative of respecting and including inside-industry energy transition skeptics because — the reality is — not everyone has bought in. Nor will they do so.

Fast Follower or Failure?

Early in my interviews for this book I spoke with David Victor, professor of innovation and public policy at the School of Global Policy and Strategy at the University of California San Diego (UCSD) — and much more. I wanted to get Victor's two cents because of his research on innovation, his leadership in decarbonization, and my respect for his pragmatic stance on the complexity of the energy transition. He had, after all written a report titled *Energy Transformations: Technology, Policy, Capital and the Murky Future of Oil and Gas*, which laid out "five iconic 'solutions'" for oil and gas companies to use to decarbonize. I expected that he could expand on his recommendations in the report.

Instead, Victor told me that oil and gas companies are fundamentally not set up to innovate in ways that the energy transition requires. He advised companies instead to work on decarbonization on the margins, in areas of relevant expertise, such as geothermal energy and carbon sequestration. When I pressed him on why, he said that the culture of companies wasn't conducive to the kind of risk and adaption the energy transition does and will need.

I disagree.

Let me be clear: Victor made a compelling case. My company, Adamantine Energy, works with many of our clients to help them engage as "fast followers" on ESG and decarbonization. We recommend the fast-following path because not everyone can be on the bleeding edge of innovation on all fronts at all times. When I asked Victor about this philosophy, I expected enthusiastic agreement. Instead, he explained, "Probably the most famous fast follower in history was Microsoft." Microsoft let other companies take the risk, watched who died off, and mimicked the success stories. He continued, "Fast following is a strategy that works when you can observe in the outside world the key lessons from working with a new technology or a new business — and you can quickly internalize those [lessons] and scale them." But, Victor went on to caution, "most of what's transformative in the oil and gas industry isn't like that." He explained that the energy transition requires a *total* transformation using new technologies, in novel ways, in unprecedented business models. And this total transformation, he said, is not practical for incumbent firms that must also manage their existing, base businesses. It's a classic illustration of the core quandary of Clayton Christensen's *The Innovator's Dilemma*. Victor explained that successful firms are "very good at making advances inside their industry, but then they get trapped there." In other words, "there is a fast follower's dilemma," said

Victor, which is that companies *think* they're good at innovating, but they are really equipped to innovate only within their own domains, where fast following works.

This argument is compelling, and much of the world believes it. But I've written *Real Decarbonization* because it's wrong.

Energy system decarbonization will happen better, faster, and more affordably with the oil and gas industry at the helm. I've had a career working in and with the oil and gas industry. Through running Adamantine Energy, I've been working directly with executive teams on future-proofing our industry for the better part of a decade. And I have spent four years interviewing leaders in and around the oil and gas industry to understand what is driving them to prioritize energy transition work—the work I call "real decarbonization," to distinguish it from the theoretical kind most pundits toss around. Throughout this book I will reference my conversations — some confidential, most credited — with the leaders who generously informed my argument about oil, gas, and our path to real decarbonization. Through my regular work, these interviews, and the additional research conducted for this book, I am certain that not only *can* the oil and gas industry lead the energy transition, we *must*.

You don't need to agree. But you do need to develop a real decarbonization strategy.

Skeptics: The Ways You Are Right

In early 2022, a Fortune 500 oil and gas CEO asked me, "Tisha, isn't the world done putting climate first?" And at midyear, another CEO asked me, "Haven't your fundamental ideas been proven wrong, Tisha? Aren't you rethinking the pressures driving the industry?" Skeptics: You are in good company!

After all, Russia invaded Ukraine in early 2022, and the subsequent Western-imposed sanctions on Russia threatened global energy supplies, creating shortages and exacerbating price spikes.

Suddenly European and North American governments became passionate about producing more oil and gas! And oil and gas supporters reveled in the public's realizations about (1) the important role of oil and gas today, (2) the imperative of producing oil and gas in North America, and (3) the complexity of the energy transition.

And CEOs peppered me with hard-edged questions about whether we were done with all this energy transition business.

Clearly, the world requires more energy than ever before. Global events have made it strikingly apparent that oil and gas resources are needed everywhere, for the foreseeable future. Oil and gas company leaders are in a vise: called to supply more oil and gas while simultaneously being vilified for producing fossil fuels.

That vise is certainly frustrating. Policymakers and pundits alike peddle a mythical near-term future where oil and gas are no longer needed. While I do believe that climate-hawk leaders are sincere, I think they convey a vision of the short-term energy future built on magical thinking. Their imagined short-term future free of oil and gas resources requires a full-scale rebuild of our energy system, relies on technologies that do not yet exist, and oversimplifies the myriad complexities of the energy system. This is *not* real decarbonization.

So, skeptics, you are right. The world needs more oil and gas than ever before. The energy transition will be long, fraught, complicated, and expensive. Oil and gas are the lifeblood of our prosperous existence.

You Need a Real Decarbonization Strategy

You need a real decarbonization strategy anyway.

Our industry is destined to evolve, as all industries must. Technological disruptions are inevitable, requiring our companies to modernize. Great company leaders are going to lead great companies, not play politics. Let's look at each of these propositions.

The entrepreneurial spirit and ingenuity that have allowed our industry to change the world in so many positive ways over the last 150 years will still be required for the next 30 — and the decades that follow. Oil and gas companies will deliver different goods and services, evolving as technology and consumer expectations change.

We also know that dramatic disturbance of the energy system is inevitable. Disruptions will come from many directions, but innovations and efficiencies are happening today at breakneck pace. Savvy, forward-thinking leaders strive to be both nimble and opportunistic in this moment. Listen to how Rob Sadler, group vice president for energy transition and transformation at DCP Midstream, put decarbonization into the context of a continuous trajectory of modernizing: "We strongly believe that the businesses that will survive and flourish, and will exist a decade from now, will, very simply, be the most profitable and the cleanest."

Working within this landscape of entrepreneurship and disruption, company leaders cannot let personal belief systems or political identities be their guide. As Alan Armstrong, CEO of Williams Companies, said when I asked him about his approach to addressing climate: "It's irresponsible to take on climate change solely from a personal perspective. Objectively, as a professional, your job is to make sure that you're leading the company in a way that is valuable for its shareholders and its employees and its stakeholders in the long run. So personal perspective shouldn't dictate how you run a company." He went on to describe his approach: Sure, our industry is not entirely responsible for carbon emissions, but are we responsible for some? So it doesn't really matter if our industry is treated fairly or unjustly vilified: We have a responsibility to serve as societal leaders.

Before my interviews, I thought I would need to create a place in this book for the oil and gas company that plans to maintain the status quo. After all, isn't just keeping a business delivering on its operational priorities enough for the inevitably volatile next 10 years? One executive convinced me otherwise: "That's the only posture that I think is certain to fail. Because if you believe that the energy transition is all going to go away, that is a proxy [for] saying, 'We're comfortable in our existing business model. And by the way, as far forward as we see, we can imagine no high levels of change.' The players that are making profound changes to their business models will outcompete the players that think this is all going away."

And so even if you hate the idea of a real decarbonization strategy, you need to understand that great company leaders such as Sadler and Armstrong know that change is inevitable — and they are responding to it. To join them, your job is to harness (1) the 150 years of the entrepreneurial spirit that defines oil and gas, (2) the sector's equally persistent drive to evolve and modernize, and (3) the imperative to lead while leaving your personal politics out of it.

After all, with disruption come new needs and novel opportunities. Company leaders can and should prepare their organizations for the energy transition in a way that simultaneously addresses political pressure to decarbonize, the perennial quest to modernize, and the need to provide value to shareholders.

Which gets me back to the quote from Williams's Chad Zamarin, who is senior vice president for corporate strategic development, that kicked off this chapter. We must never forget that oil and gas leaders are overwhelmingly scientists and engineers, who love to solve problems. Throughout this book, you'll hear from oil and gas industry executives with one common point of view: They see the opportunity to contribute solutions to the energy transition. (While there are plenty of downsides to working in a world dominated by engineers, this is a serious upside!) The current political polarization around climate and energy is intense — so intense that climate hawks are keeping solutions off the table. But there are real decarbonization solutions, and our industry can provide them.

Toby Rice, president and CEO of EQT Corporation, is a great example of an oil and gas problem-solver. He knows how the industry has historically resisted the energy transition: "A lot of the people in this industry ... In the past, it's been a boxing match," he said.

"It's been fighting against renewables." But Rice decided his company would take a different approach by "taking people's concerns and moving with that and addressing that," he told me. EQT's "biggest green initiative on the planet" takes stakeholders' interest in climate and proposes a solution within his company's sweet spot, "unleashing" U.S. liquefied natural gas (LNG). And he approaches industry allies and opponents alike, asking for open mindedness. "Being closed-minded," he told me, "is not going to be a mentality that's going to enable us to innovate to these solutions."

Energy company leaders have three choices in to address the energy transition: (1) inform and participate in the disruption, (2) react to the pressure to decarbonize, or (3) sit on the sidelines and get left behind. The greatest takeaway from my work: It doesn't matter how you feel about the energy transition. This isn't about identity or politics. The energy transition is underway. Leaders see opportunity. Leaders see the imperative.

You sit on the sidelines at your peril.

Why You Need a 10-Year Real Decarbonization Strategy

"Most people overestimate what they can do in one year and underestimate what they can do in 10 years."

— Bill Gates

It is not a given that any company will be around in 10 years.

Whatever historic moment you are in when you are reading this book, that moment will always involve a few constants for the energy industry:

- Consumers will continue to expect always on, abundant, and affordable energy.
- Production and delivery of energy will continue to become cleaner and more sustainable.
- Technology and innovation will be advancing.

Regardless of the state of politics or partisanship or passion, as Alan Armstrong of Williams puts it, "The way we've been running business for the last 30 years is not going to work for the next 30 years."

Now, I happen to believe that voters, policymakers, and consumers will continue to prioritize addressing climate change. And, as we covered in Chapter 1, you don't have to believe in climate change to understand the urgency of developing your 10-year real decarbonization strategy — and to start developing it. Looking at the volatility around geopolitics, domestic partisanship, commodity prices, and macroeconomics tells us that oil and gas company leaders must be poised for change — a lot of it. To paraphrase Wouter van Kempen, CEO of DCP Midstream: The cycles of volatility are getting shorter, the swings more violent.

Why have I made 10 years the target for your real decarbonization strategy? Because it's a time frame that provides balance between (1) enough time to make deep, structural changes that will transform the business and (2) a short enough runway to create accountability with employees, investors, and stakeholders who want to see a plan that connects aspiration with verifiable action.

Volatility and Transformation

The Number 1 reason you need a 10-year real decarbonization strategy: The world is volatile and transforming on an unprecedented scale. Its volatility and transformation provide you with the opportunity of a lifetime to act — to seize energy leadership. But if you don't act, volatility and transformation will quickly present your company with a series of existential threats. Consider what Mark Brownstein, senior vice president of energy at the Environmental Defense Fund (EDF), recently told me: "EDF is an environmental NGO [nongovernmental organization] with a satellite that will enable us to, on a regular basis, assess emissions for more than 80 percent of global oil and gas operations. The technology exists to not only collect that data but make it widely available." This new level of data and visibility is just one example of the avalanche of change coming for the oil and gas industry.

David Victor of UCSD opined on the exponential nature of disruption, explaining, "People have a very hard time processing … the implications of a system that could scale very, very rapidly. If we were in IT, then we would have no problem with that, because the whole business is a series of revolutions, and every two years the incumbent idea dies, something new comes along, and Google buys it." He's quite transparent, admitting that he doesn't know if the energy transition will happen that quickly, but he is certain that oil and gas executives need to prepare: "I think the real skill in this business comes from identifying those signposts that tell you you've got a real revolution here," he said, "as opposed to the 97 revolutions that were predicted and didn't actually happen."

In a world where the only certainty is uncertainty, industry leaders own a few planning imperatives:

- Expect disruption in numerous forms: technology, the economy, politics, commodity pricing, the supply chain, geopolitics, public opinion, and generational and stakeholder expectations.
- Build a nimble organization responsive to changing conditions.
- Instill resilience in your company culture.
- Seek out likely new opportunities through envisioning and planning exercises.
- Play offense through proactive positioning in emerging arenas, such as hydrogen and renewable natural gas.
- Consider all the ways in which you can shape your company's transformation through your engagement and actions.

For an energy company to be relevant in 10 years, it will have to have done more than survive the inevitable twists and turns. Because the twists and turns of the next decade will be, as van Kempen put it, frequent and dramatic. Toby Rice of EQT translates this into opportunity: "The holy grail that everyone is looking for in energy is cheap, reliable, zero-carbon energy. And I don't care if you're in nuclear, you're in solar, you're in wind, you're in oil and gas, you're in biodiesel. If you're in energy, the ultimate prize is figuring out how to make cheap, reliable, zero-carbon energy." A successful leader will execute forward-thinking strategic moves while tending to the resilience of the core business.

Pendulum Swing or Directional Change?

Energy company executives have ridden the twists and turns the 2020s have presented so far with a mix of optimism and realism. The politics, pandemic waves, and several energy price crises of the decade have raised these questions for oil and gas leaders: Will the pendulum of public opinion swing back on the urgency of climate change, putting oil and gas once again back in public favor? Or have we embarked upon an inevitable *directional change* — a train moving inexorably toward a net-zero society?

Rice of EQT told me that engagement with climate change is table stakes for energy leaders: "To be an energy executive today, you need to understand climate, because it is a big thing that's pressing against your business." But he sees that pressure not as a fundamental threat but a fundamental opportunity. "The more I read about this, the more conviction I have that if the world wants to meet its climate goals, the world needs the energy industry; they need oil and gas to get in here and do it." What a clear example he gives of the historic optimism, problem-solving, and entrepreneurship of oil and gas leaders.

But why does Rice see the pressure to decarbonize as a huge opportunity for oil and gas? "If you want to win the race to zero carbon, you want to win that energy transition — we have the best vehicle to do that," Rice said. "Because guess what? We have a track record of dealing with crisis and actually going through an energy transition." Rice invoked the "peak oil" crisis, which was answered by the shale revolution 20 years ago. "What did this industry do to respond?" he recalled. "We went through a transition. We transitioned from drilling and developing conventional reservoirs to drilling unconventional reservoirs: shale. And how did we do that? It was amazing technology, amazing innovation, amazing risk-taking, and collaboration."

If, like Rice, you view climate pressure as an opportunity, it removes the temptation to overemphasize political pendulum swings. Ever since Russia invaded Ukraine in early 2022, many energy observers have been predicting that the renewed global focus on energy security would signal an end to the global focus on climate change. I disagree with those energy observers, but we share at least this judgment: Politics moves like a pendulum, swinging back and forth from one extreme to another.

Many reasonable people could (but don't) agree that the energy–environment pendulum has swung too far in the address-climate-at-all-costs direction. I certainly think it has. In a world with a lot of global challenges and priorities, the climate-apocalypse narrative certainly doesn't work for all of us — not even many climate hawks.

Yet that doesn't mean that the pendulum will swing back to a pre-2020 world.

Four significant structural changes over the past decade indicate that global interest in climate is directional. And, although at times we experience a political pendulum correction, we shouldn't mistake pendulum corrections for directional change. Climate and decarbonization pressures aren't on a pendulum; they are on a train. The train may slow, but it is inexorably on its way to climate town.

And that's an opportunity for us.

The Drivers of Directional Change

The four structural changes that drive directional climate action are mobilizing — and will continue to mobilize — public interest in climate:

- **Investor pressure.** Now that everyone from BlackRock CEO Larry Fink to U.S. Treasury Secretary Janet Yellen to the Securities and Exchange Commission has equated climate risk with financial risk, responsible investors must begin prioritizing climate initiatives. A continuous flow of investor queries and proposed regulations reinforces how central climate analyses will be to company operations and disclosures. As one executive explained, "One of the most important outcomes of COP26 was this notion that net zero is an organizing principle for business." Net-zero planning — building a strategy that has your company's emissions zero out through offsets or negative emissions — has become an investor expectation.

- **Public sentiment.** Stakeholders tend to interpret current events through their own political lenses. For example, in early 2022 I sat on a panel where one participant said the war in Ukraine was accelerating Germany's permitting of wind facilities and another pointed out that Germany was turning coal-fired power back on. Very few people rewrite their climate analyses in the face of world events; many use world events to double down on their climate priorities. Even greater disruptions won't disrupt their habits of seeing.

- **Generational change.** The oldest millennials are now in their early 40s and continue to take leadership positions across finance, politics, community organizations, and business. They will dominate the population beyond 2050. Gen Z has now joined the millennials in the workforce; together these two cohorts will soon constitute most working adults. Members of these generations, even when politically conservative, often prioritize climate — and that prioritization is not going to change.

- **Company recruiting and retention.** For the foreseeable future, oil and gas companies will be competing to both recruit and retain millennial and Gen Z talent. And increasingly, millennial and Gen Z workers will be under pressure from their peers to be a part of the climate solution (or at least part of the industries of the future!). Ask them and they will tell you: They want to see their companies leading in the decarbonizing energy future. And they will continue to pressure you to do so.

The drivers of directional change have resulted in changing expectations for oil and gas companies — from both within and without. These changing expectations include everything from lower-methane-intensity natural gas to detailed climate-scenario analyses on business risk. And these changing expectations are intensifying.

Changing Expectations

As expectations continue to rise for oil and gas companies' participation in real decarbonization activities, companies themselves are leading the charge. Case in point: The Oil and Gas Climate Initiative comprises 12 of the world's largest oil and gas companies, all of which have committed to reduce methane emissions significantly. Brownstein of EDF told me, "Those 12 companies represent over a third of global oil and gas production." That is the decarbonization train in action.

In my last book, *The Gamechanger's Playbook*, I advocated for companies to set aspirational decarbonization goals and to share those goals, as well as their vision and values, with their stakeholders. Explicit visionary leadership is mission-critical to changing the dynamics between our industry and a skeptical-to-hostile public. As many of the leaders I interviewed for this book told me, it's nearly impossible to build any new infrastructure — from pipelines to LNG terminals — anywhere today. Companies require a vision of the future to share with communities and stakeholders to create new conversations about why any energy production, transportation, or delivery system gets built.

Since 2020, when I wrote *The Gamechanger's Playbook*, having an energy transition aspiration has become necessary for oil and gas companies — but also insufficient. Investors, customers, and employees now expect action.

This expectation of action stems from the structural drivers I mentioned in the previous section, but it also takes us quickly into more complex territory. No one wants to be stuck in the past, and an interesting aspect of the politics of energy and climate is that oil and gas have been caricatured as the fuels of the past. Furthermore, status quo energy-climate politics assumes that oil and gas companies are insincere about decarbonizing the energy system. These two baseline assumptions about oil and gas mean that your company's efforts to decarbonize are often greeted with a quagmire of emotional responses — among everyone from employees to consumers.

Employees are an excellent audience to start with to evaluate the changing expectations of energy companies, because they are our frontline interface with other stakeholders. Now more than ever, employees find themselves acting as ambassadors for their companies and for the industry as a whole. Their situation is made easier by companies with meaningful real decarbonization strategies. Leaders I interviewed whose companies had explicit decarbonization strategies described an enthusiastic employee response. Employees had conveyed to these leaders that, as employees, they wanted to participate in energy evolution leadership for a number of reasons:

- They feel pride in being a part of the climate solution and building the energy future, particularly those with grandchildren. They consider this work part of their legacy.
- They see energy transition jobs as the future of work, whether it's the digitalization of existing operations or entirely new business ventures.
- They experience social pressure because they work for an oil and gas company. This is especially true of millennial and Gen Z employees, who often feel they have to justify

working in our sector. Energy transition work allows them to tell a compelling story about our role in addressing climate.

- They want to be a part of finding the solutions to this monumental challenge of climate and decarbonization. This desire is particularly acute in engineering and technically trained staff.

As Matt Kolesar, chief environmental scientist at ExxonMobil, put it to me as we talked about how other Exxon employees engage him in his energy work: "Universally, it's 'I want to be a part of the solution,' [or] 'I want to be part of the energy transition.'" Rob Sadler of DCP Midstream characterized millennials' attitude toward their work: "'I've got to believe in what we're doing. And if I believe in what we're doing, I'll throw myself in headfirst, and I'll throw myself out into the world advocating for it.'"

In this realm of changing expectations, *all* energy-climate work is political — and you as an oil and gas leader must convey your vision of the energy future within that political context. No one has done this more explicitly than Rice. Rice and EQT took both policymakers' and the public's sense of urgency on climate and proposed the fastest, most pragmatic solution: dramatically expanding LNG exports from the United States to displace international coal. "I think to be successful we have to say, 'What is the biggest, most impactful thing that's going to make a difference, and let's focus there,'" he told me. On the transition away from coal, Rice has tremendous urgency. "We are not moving fast enough along that path," he said. "And what that means is every day that we don't make significant progress, we have to accelerate. ... It just makes it even harder." Rice told me he sees all this work as part of the same decarbonization train: "But on that 'Unleash LNG' [initiative] there's an asterisk behind 'Unleash,'" he said. "And that asterisk is a commitment to net-zero operations. So that's going to be really important: net-zero production, net-zero midstream, net-zero LNG manufacturing."

This is real decarbonization — the kind of ambition for energy leadership within the transition that creates a new kind of conversation, forcing climate hawks to ask themselves, "Am I more committed to the fight with oil and gas or to progress on climate?" Our job today is to pursue progress relentlessly and optimistically. And a company cannot meaningfully demonstrate its plan to act without a thoughtful strategy — a 10-year real decarbonization strategy.

Keeping Options Open

Even if a company has infinite innovation and investment resources, its leaders do not have any certainty that policymakers, regulators, and stakeholders will allow the permitting, construction, and operation of any new energy project. Building a 10-year energy plan now adds important risk mitigation to your company's resilience strategy. This mitigation covers two primary arenas: (1) keeping development options open and (2) influencing relevant policy factors.

Let's take hydrogen development as an option. Leaders within and outside of industry have generally assumed that future decarbonization projects (such as hydrogen) would be met with open arms by policymakers and stakeholders. This has not been the case.

If you've been around oil and gas for any time at all, you've probably bought into the adage "If you're not at the table, you're on the menu." But what's worse than being on the menu? Not being in the restaurant at all!

Growing opposition to hydrogen development provides a stark warning to industry leaders. Academics and activists are working to turn the public and policymakers against decarbonization strategies that are perceived as benefiting the oil and gas industry. If we want to keep policy doors open for these strategies — for decarbonizing fuels, carbon capture and sequestration (CCS), and hydrogen — company leaders will need to assertively engage in the conversations about them immediately. Having a 10-year real decarbonization strategy is an essential framework to guide your research, partnerships, and engagement efforts.

In my experience, oil and gas companies are inclined to pursue decarbonization opportunities quietly, wanting to prove them up before making announcements or commitments. This "quiet" strategy is no longer effective; we don't want to see our industry decarbonization strategies obsolete before we have even imagined their full fruition. The lesson: Make it part of your 10-year strategy to both announce and engage on decarbonization initiatives now, to ensure that future decarbonization options are not foreclosed on by damning policy or public opinion.

Whether it's our stance on directional change on climate or the potential for opposition to CCS, Maynard Holt, founder and CEO at Veriten, told me our rationality about the social reality on climate and energy creates massive blind spots for our industry. "One blind spot we all have is saying certain ideas are not rational or don't make sense," he said. "When we have that moment, we have to remind ourselves: There have always been lots of ideas that didn't make sense, until suddenly they did." Keeping options open requires paying attention to, engaging with, and informing the public and policymakers about the energy transition — not dismissing them because we "know better."

And then there's the untapped, potential upside of a wide-open playing field. As Armstrong of Williams puts it, "What should the rules be if we want to win at a different game?" Armstrong is looking at the energy transition through a wide aperture: Are there policy and pricing innovations that have yet to be defined that will accelerate the energy transition, save consumers money, and allow companies to be profitable? Company leaders with a 10-year real decarbonization strategy can expand their vision to everything from supply chain to delivery innovations. This wide lens gives them a broad area for engaging in policy discussions — ultimately allowing more opportunities for creating win-wins.

Status Quo or 10-Year Energy Strategy?

In many ways, Rice has a real decarbonization strategy for EQT that rejects the status quo without changing the company's base business. Here is how he put it to me, passionately: "As long as we are burning wood, dung, and coal in this world, then there is an opportunity to evolve the fuel that people are using to natural gas, which means that there is a need in this world for EQT and the product that we produce." The EQT approach puts climate concern at its center, with that stance's potential to draw in skeptical stakeholders. And Rice is confident in that strategy's appeal. "'Unleash U.S. LNG' is going to launch the biggest green initiative on the planet," he told me. "It's going to cost the government and the American taxpayer zero dollars. We'll do it because it truly is a sustainable solution."

Change is everywhere — and when change is everywhere, maintaining the status quo is not an option. As one leader conveyed, defending the status quo as your path forward is now the equivalent of saying, "As far as we can see into the future, we do not see any meaningful change." Taking that stance turns your blind spot into blindness itself.

So we end this chapter essentially where we started it: Building a 10-year real decarbonization strategy is necessary, because change is inevitable, and successful companies will plan and pivot. You'll see as you proceed through this book that many traditional oil and gas companies are already doing so. I was struck, for example, when Chad Zamarin of Williams related an encounter with one of his employees to me:

> *Williams has been around for 100 years, and we've had to evolve many times throughout that 100-year history. I talked to an employee here this morning who asked me, "What do you envision our company being in 2120?" That's not a question many companies in our space ask themselves. We were here in 1920. And the things we were doing in 1920*

aren't the things we're doing in 2022. And we want to be here in 2120. And things that we're going to do today have an influence on what we're going to do in the future. So what do I need to do today to keep moving toward the company that I want to be in the future? If you embrace this idea of change, then you expect an evolution of some kind.

A 100-year strategy isn't for everyone, but a 10-year one is certainly a reasonable place to start. Companies that do not have one are watching the train leave the station. All aboard!

CHAPTER 3

Where to Start

"'What if we get it right?' That's the conversation we should be in."

– Paula Gant, GTI Energy

The executives I interviewed for this book clearly agree on this point: Any company embarking on energy transition planning from a defensive or reactionary mindset will not succeed. This consensus surprised me, because I thought the likely readers of this book might have just such a mindset. (Not *you*, dear reader — the others!) Because I often work with the oil and gas "fast follower," I imagined that it might well have been an activist investor or a particularly strong-minded board member who drove you or your executive team to pick up this book. Even if that's the case, you'll have to soon develop your own set of reasons for building your company's 10-year real decarbonization strategy. Oil and gas leaders who are already doing this work told me over and over that strong drivers are key to engagement. So no matter what drove you to pick up this book, you can find those drivers and set a successful course.

Build the Team

If you're like me, you'd just as soon take out a pencil and a blank piece of paper and start articulating the objectives of your 10-year strategy on your own. Go for it! Just keep that brilliant, self-derived plan under wraps for a bit.

The foundation of your successful plan will be a strong assessment of your current conditions, stakeholder drivers, and possible courses of action. This assessment will be as good as the bright minds you assign to it and the resources you give them, including time, money, access, and authority. So pull together a team and give them a strong, effective, and collaborative leader. Have that leader report as high up in the organization as you can stand, preferably to the C-suite. As you'll see, the team will have a bit of work to do, and that work will need your full support.

Take Stock

Throughout the rest of this book, we will tackle the components of company organization, culture, and planning that are mission-critical to building an effective real decarbonization strategy. To make the most of future company efforts, leaders must first conduct an honest assessment of the strongest elements of their core business and the weakest links in their operational practices. As the company leaders I interviewed discussed the lessons they learned from undertaking real decarbonization, they emphasized that the stress of energy transition initiatives has meant they've had to rely heavily on company strengths to provide scaffolding and stability for these new efforts. Similarly, their companies' weak links — whether in finances, in health and safety culture, or in operational excellence — tended to provoke exaggerated impacts in new company initiatives.

A company's real decarbonization strategy will more or less fall into one of these trajectories:

1. **Produce and provide the last, cheapest oil and gas.**
   Companies following this trajectory are planning to
   continue their traditional businesses, with a focus on
   efficiency and cost and with a nod to the environmental
   sustainability required to manage their social risk. You
   can imagine, say, an oil pipeline company operating in
   a friendly jurisdiction that wants to put its head down
   and do just what needs to be done. Such companies
   will focus on operational efficiency and reducing their
   environmental footprint.

2. **Create the lowest-carbon oil and gas resource.**
   Companies looking to invest in carbon-neutral and
   carbon-negative businesses while remaining fundamentally
   oil and gas companies will still have much work to do.

3. **Diversify the business.** Companies on this trajectory
   (which include many international oil and gas companies
   in particular) are building a mixed energy business,
   providing some traditional oil and gas resources and
   building new businesses such as hydrogen production,
   electric vehicle charging, and offshore wind production.

4. **Build a new energy company.** Finally, some companies
   are looking to get out of oil and gas altogether, switching
   to zero-carbon electric generation or all new net-zero
   energy services.

Most readers of this book are probably working for companies
that follow one of the first two trajectories, with an eye to opportunities in the third. Taking stock of where your company is situated is an
iterative process. My advice: Work through the rest of the sections in
this chapter on getting started, consider your ambitions in Chapter 4,
and then return to see if what you have in place will support your
likely direction.

This chapter identifies areas for your real decarbonization planning team to take stock of in determining your company's starting point, including leadership commitment, base business strength, employee and stakeholder priorities, company culture, risk posture, and public ESG commitments.

But first, let's see if your glass is half full.

An Optimistic Exercise

CEOs by nature seem to be glass-half-full kind of people. You wouldn't necessarily know this unless you asked them about what they find to be toughest in their work. In my interviews, CEOs and their network of strategic allies continually reframed my negatively framed questions into opportunity-filled answers.

Dominic Emery, who was serving as bp CEO Bernard Looney's chief of staff when I interviewed him and was formerly vice president of bp's strategic planning group, took the initiative early in our conversation to reframe the demands of the energy transition on his company in terms of the opportunity:

> To replumb and rewire the world's energy system is going to cost something like $2 trillion to $3 trillion every year for the next 30 years. Other commentators suggest it may even be two or three times that. Whatever it is, it's a phenomenal investment that's going to be required — and an extraordinary business opportunity. The key is to see this through an optimistic and opportunity-driven lens rather than as an existential threat.

How does this optimism typically and specifically manifest itself in real decarbonization planning? Several priorities emerged from my conversations:

- **Shared benefits.** Leaders need to develop a real decarbonization strategy that identifies and amplifies co-benefits to the company, its shareholders, its communities, and its customers. They also need to emphasize those shared benefits throughout the work to maintain the support of those constituencies.

- **Back to business.** Energy transition initiatives are *business* initiatives; they aren't a side hustle or overhead. They must be framed as part of your entire organization's operational positioning.

- **Planning horizon.** Fundamentally, energy transition planning is *business* planning. Company leaders are tasked with imagining how they will position their companies to maximize overall success over the next planning horizon — and 10-year real decarbonization strategies should be front and center in their positioning and planning.

In energy transition planning, a positive and holistic framing will be critical to ultimate success. Although there is a time and place for bite-sized progress, this initiative requires vision and optimism. Fortunately, such vision and optimism are part of our heritage as industry leaders. Proceed accordingly!

What If I'm Just an Employee?

Company evolution requires a healthy push-pull between the layers and across the organizations within a company. Leaders know that everything important done by the company *is done by the people in the company.* And thinking deeply about the challenges the energy transition poses to your company is smart work for employees.

Most of the peanut gallery out there opining on what oil and gas companies should be doing dramatically oversimplify … well, everything. Even well-intentioned employees impatient to see company action on real decarbonization are likely to underestimate the effort required and oversimplify the complexity of such a massive endeavor.

This book will guide you to think holistically, pragmatically, and deeply about what your organization needs to consider in developing its 10-year real decarbonization strategy. And your journey in reading it will position you to be both a keen observer of company plans and uniquely poised to suggest action.

Company leaders whom I interviewed expressed genuine delight with the responses they were receiving from across their organizations in support of their various energy transition ventures. They recognized the village-like nature of their organizations' communities, frequenting saying things like "Our best ideas to execute these goals have repeatedly come from the field," "I certainly don't have all the answers — I'm counting on our bright minds to figure out the details," and "We need a mix of experienced, traditional employees with our new-ideas folks to find solutions that will actually be able to navigate our bureaucracy." As someone who works with oil and gas leaders daily, I can assure you that they mean every word.

I think Chad Zamarin of Williams summarized the opportunity for employees best: "There's a lot of footballs lying on the field right now. Who's going to pick one up and just start running?"

Leadership Commitment

A company's energy transition efforts will not be successful without the CEO's explicit commitment. There were zero exceptions to this rule in my interviews with company leaders.

Furthermore, energy transition work *is difficult, requires years,* and *will face many headwinds.* I observed that successful CEOs and key transition leaders developed their own, internal understanding of why they are embarking upon and enduring this work. Leaders would often convey a private origin story for their commitment and a very personal motivation for taking on the challenge. One CEO spoke of his adult children and their expectations of him. Another conveyed his responsibility to his employees and shareholders: "My personal feelings about climate are irrelevant. I have a duty to the future of this business."

Toby Rice of EQT provided a great example of such an origin story: "It really starts with our higher purpose. You know, when we sold our first company, Rice Energy, our higher purpose back then was to help bring energy independence to America." As he moved to EQT during the original merger, out into semi-retirement, and then back into EQT as its CEO, a higher purpose — evolving throughout his journey, but always there — remained his touchstone. "Making a positive impact on the world really is the motivation," he told me. "The higher purpose for us at EQT is really two things. It's to provide energy security to the world while also helping arrest climate change. And so 'Unleashing U.S. LNG' is an initiative that's going to allow us to achieve both of those higher-purpose goals."

CEOs will tell you that they must have their boards behind them, but for energy transition work, I heard another common theme: CEOs and company executives started with a vision and a value proposition for their programs and strategies that *they took to their boards*. Although CEOs will not explicitly talk about how they bring along their boards, that's exactly what they do.

Board support for any high-level initiative is, of course, mission-critical. But the board that drives a real decarbonization strategy is rare. I would not recommend waiting for your board. If a board has to bring you along to get the energy transition work done, my guess is you won't be there very long.

Once a company board has bought in to the need for a real decarbonization strategy, it often retools to bring in new expertise or points of view to support the strategic direction. This retooling is a natural evolution, part of the changes you will make as you assess your company's baseline capabilities, reconsider resources and missing expertise, and return with your likely strategic direction.

Emery of bp conveyed the particular importance of your leadership's being all in as you set out to build a real decarbonization strategy:

My advice is that there is no point starting on decarbonization, greening, and transitioning unless there is absolute conviction that it's the right thing to do at the top of the house — the board and the executive team. To go ahead with such an undertaking without having that level of support would be unwise. It may be better just to stick to the knitting if you haven't got conviction. If there's no appetite, excitement, and curiosity about what this opportunity can deliver, don't even start.

As you take stock of your company's readiness for this work, you must do an early assessment of the strength, conviction, and depth of leadership for the transition. If you don't have leadership conviction, make this book mandatory reading. Nobody wants to stick to the knitting.

Culture

To succeed, a decarbonization strategy must both draw on and fuel company culture. When your real decarbonization strategy and your company's culture support each other, two things happen: (1) Your employees will be both empowered by and excited about the strategy's vision of the future, and (2) they will contribute to the strategy as only those close to the ground can. Your organization's people are so vital to strategic success that I've devoted Chapter 5 to the topic.

Alice Jackson, senior vice president for system strategy and chief planning officer at Xcel Energy, has seen that empowerment firsthand: "That over-the-horizon goal can be really motivating for employees to look at: What are the possibilities? What are the technologies?" she told me. Rob Sadler of DCP Midstream described for me how to put that empowerment into play: "In order for us to be successful in decarbonizing our business, the progress gets made in the field," he explained. "The ideas come from the people who oftentimes turn the wrenches. ... And our ability to make progress means that we have to execute on every level."

Here are two big reasons why company culture is so important to real decarbonization success:

- Strengths and weaknesses of company culture will get amplified under the stress of decarbonization implementation.
- The systems to organize and implement your strategy must align with key cultural elements or they will fail.

For this assessment, the type of culture isn't the heart of the matter. Companies can be wildly successful with a range of cultures. Rice of EQT builds his culture from the company's higher purpose: "Our product brings peace, it brings prosperity, it brings jobs, and it provides quality of life," he told me. "I've learned from the very beginning: To really drive engagement, our people need to be working with the knowledge that it's not all motivated by dollars. We are not coin-operated. We have heart, and we want to make sure that people know that there's a greater good for the work that we're doing."

Paula Gant, CEO of GTI Energy, told me about how she organizes her teams around a shared objective with broadly distributed accountability to solve consequential problems. She explained, "Rather than telling people what to do, I want to inspire them to think differently, to ask new questions and write new rules." This process, she said, "helps them align around an objective and engage each other's strengths, and creates the running room they need to get to goal while championing the effort along the way."

Individual employees often gravitate to companies with a good culture match, so the specific type of culture isn't what will ultimately determine success — it is the *strength* and *pervasiveness* of the culture. Use the following questions to assess the strength of your company's culture.

- **Are our values pervasive?** Whether formal or informal, companies with authentic and pervasive core values can use these values to drive change.
- **Is our culture consistent across divisions and throughout the hierarchy?** Energy transition work will create new tensions and perceived or actual inequities across operational groups. Companies with strong identity and trust across the organization are better positioned to navigate through these inevitable icebergs.
- **Do our employees frequently and thematically talk about our culture?** In a strong culture, employees throughout the organization will talk about the culture consistently and thematically.

Maynard Holt of Veriten emphasized to me the virtuous cycle of a strong company culture: "Over time, people of a certain culture are attracted to companies that have that culture, so every year, you're adding people who were drawn to the culture you've created. Culture continually reinforces itself — good and bad."

Once a real decarbonization strategy is underway, its communication and execution will require the inclusion of participants across operations, divisions, branches, and levels. Their input and buy-in will require broad engagement. In my firm's work with companies embarking on even small-scale ESG and decarbonization efforts, we have observed how the strength of a company's culture influences the success of such efforts. Take a clear-eyed look at your company culture as it is today and address its weaknesses in order to prepare for the work ahead.

Base Business and Financials

Energy transition work is most often additive to your current base business or businesses. Although the initial work is often about reducing emissions or creating efficiencies, even those require upfront investment. Begin this work, then, with an honest assessment of your current business strengths and weaknesses, with an eye to the stresses you already know are ahead.

Occidental Petroleum is one of the largest oil producers in the United States with significant chemicals, midstream, and marketing businesses. Vicki Hollub, Occidental's president and CEO, must balance this base business with a significant, relatively new business unit for low-carbon ventures. "That is a challenge that we must get right," she told me. "And that's because we have to deliver value to our shareholders. And so the oil and gas business, our chemicals business, our midstream and marketing business: All of those need to deliver — and to deliver at a very high level. And they're doing that today, so we can't lose focus on the base business."

Very early in their real decarbonization efforts, companies will have to communicate to their employees and shareholders who is getting resources, what is getting squeezed, and how incentives are being managed. This messaging will inevitably cause flare-ups of old tensions and create new ones. Understand your company's starting point by asking these questions:

- What are we good at?
- What skills do we have?
- Is our base business strong enough to allow for investment in new efforts?
- Where are our financial strengths and weaknesses?
- What already requires more investment to achieve success?

Rice of EQT told me he thinks of his initiative in the context of his base business: "'Unleash U.S. LNG' is an energy transition plan. But the biggest differentiator between this plan and others in the past is that this plan is truly sustainable. And sustainability is the ultimate goal. And I'm not just talking about the environment. I'm talking about sustainability — meaning it's profitable. And we believe that we can put natural gas on the doorsteps of Europe for a cost of $9 [MMBtu], and that would imply a $4 gas price here in the United States."

Ultimately, your new strategy will look at the biggest potential returns on various investments. In many cases, today's core businesses will support these new investments until they can become profitable. Take stock of the strengths inherent in your base business to understand the runway and resources available to support new ventures.

Real Stakeholder Engagement

Much as it does a materiality assessment for an ESG strategy, your team will need to take stock of where your internal and external stakeholders stand on energy transition issues. Part of taking stock will include reviewing what you know your stakeholders care about. As you develop your plans, you may decide that a formal engagement effort with stakeholders would be a prudent investment of time and resources.

After all, the success of your real decarbonization strategy will depend as much on how effectively you communicate your efforts as on how well you execute them. The fraught environment of energy and climate work is not going anywhere. Ultimately, assuring your key stakeholders that your efforts are sincere and enduring will require strong engagement with them. The real engagement work begins with your assessment and early planning.

There are several ways to get input and buy-in on your energy transition planning efforts. The scope and scale will depend on your ambition and resources. Your efforts may need to be as iterative as your plans.

When he became bp's CEO, Looney embarked on a listening tour that encompassed supporters and critics among investors, customers, governments, NGOs, academia, think tanks, and the United Nations. Early input shaped his thinking and created buy-in for the tough work ahead.

Companies can start by mapping their important stakeholders internally and externally and deciding who should have a say in informing their real decarbonization strategies. Groups to consider internally include

- Different operational functions, from corporate to field and across business lines
- Employee resource groups and emerging leaders
- External-facing functions, including investor relations and customer service

Your team is seeking to understand perspectives as well as gather interests and ideas. Holt of Veriten described how his team works within companies to open the aperture on innovative work. "In the 1980s, shale made little sense, and now, you know what happened!" he told me. "We have to be open to technologies. We have got to look at the things that don't make sense rather than dismiss them. We've got to put them up on the rack and understand them better." Gathering interests and ideas requires an inquisitive and receptive mindset.

Your team can gather information from outside partners and stakeholders via interviews or surveys, targeting groups such as

- Investors, including possible or likely activist investors
- Policymakers, elected officials, and regulators
- Community organizations, businesses, and local leaders
- Customers
- Disproportionally affected or other environmental justice (EJ) communities
- Suppliers, subcontractors, and vendors
- Environmental partners, environmental NGOs (eNGOs), or EJ activists
- Local and partner universities

The prospect of surveying internal and external stakeholders often raises the hackles of energy executives. They wonder: Why would we open a can of worms or ask for input that we may not be able to act on? The answer is simple: You don't know what your stakeholders want or expect from you until you ask. *They* might not even know what they want from you until you ask. To be effective, your real decarbonization strategy must consider what your stakeholders care about and speak directly to their participation and interest.

And just asking yields valuable co-benefits. You'll gather new ideas, build goodwill, and ultimately contribute to the buy-in you need for your efforts.

Risk Tolerance and Horizon

A priority for your early assessment should be to explicitly articulate how your organization assesses and tolerates risk. Alan Armstrong of Williams described the difference between base business risk and new-venture risk: "We're not in the business of investing in negative-return projects," he said, "but we are in the business of taking on risk-adjusted investment opportunities." Oil and gas companies know their tolerance for risk in the base business, but the risk calculus for new ventures will be different. Armstrong described the difference to me this way:

> We are an industry that will put capital at risk. It should be thoughtful and disciplined. Because we've got such a healthy business and foundation, we have the capacity to invest in things that we believe will be very good investment opportunities for our shareholders. Our venture capital team has said: "We're going to invest in some things here that could be zeros." But we also think we can invest in some things that could be home runs.

Look at the strength of your base business and the calculation by which you determine its acceptable risk. Then consider your organization's appetite for different types of risk in new ventures. This assessment will inform which real decarbonization trajectory your company will pursue as well as your framework for managing risk when making investments.

Large companies with sophisticated risk management frameworks will need to contemplate how well suited their systems are to energy transition business planning. Such assessments will be similar to those that organizations have undertaken in order to do Task Force on Climate-Related Financial Disclosures (TCFD) analyses, looking at macro factors to reconsider how they affect business risk.

The next risk baseline consideration is your time horizon for risk and returns. Energy transition efforts will undoubtedly require different ROIs, in both dollar considerations and time horizons. EQT's Rice told me he considers today's infrastructure in the context of future net-zero pipes and facilities: "What's really amazing … is this can set the table for a zero-carbon economy of the future, a hydrogen economy," he said. "Unleashing U.S. LNG gives us a reason to build an incremental 50 BCF a day's worth of pipelines. And when we build those pipelines, let's build them with the future in mind. Let's build them hydrogen-ready. And by doing that we will underwrite the costs associated with [the transition to] hydrogen."

The risk time horizon connects explicitly to today's investment in today's business. Does the incremental cost increase for a hydrogen-ready pipe make sense? Rice thinks so: "And while that ultimately will service our ability to do blue hydrogen in the future, it will also set the table for green hydrogen, pink hydrogen, gold hydrogen — all the hydrogen, whatever colors they come up, we can get in this pipe."

Whatever the nature of your current business, new energy investments will probably require new risk-reward rubrics. Carefully assess your current process, culture, tolerance, and other considerations so that you can update them with both your strategic direction and your implementation plans. Then keep moving, because nothing is riskier than maintaining the status quo.

Existing Commitments

By this time, your company has all sorts of regulatory, safety, and operational efficiency targets in place. The company has also likely kicked off its ESG program and may have associated decarbonization aspirations or commitments — some shared internally and some conveyed to stakeholders. Take the time to carefully map both public and private commitments to ensure that they are (1) incorporated into your decarbonization strategy, and (2) clarified or corrected to interact consistently with your company's strategy.

Wouter van Kempen of DCP Midstream addressed with pragmatism and good humor the interplay between existing commitments and a real decarbonization strategy: "There are more decision and data points on people's plates who are running energy companies than ever before," he told me. "And with that, there's probably a pro and a con for leaders. The pro is you have an opportunity to do more really well. And the con is you have an opportunity to make more mistakes." A mistake might mean, for example, undermining incentive plans that have been working spectacularly well.

DCP Midstream has continually built its growing environmental health and safety (EHS) and ESG components into its employee compensation strategy. It started with safety, built in emissions, and refined that to greenhouse gas intensity metrics, while also focusing on operational efficiency and the digitalization required for the company's energy transition efforts. It's important to take stock of these commitments and their role in company operations and culture. Consider DCP Midstream and van Kempen's approach: "Every single employee in our company has been rewarded in their short-term incentives, or bonus, for safety since 2008," he told me. "When we meet our safety goals, our people get paid more as part of their bonus. If we don't meet our goals, our people don't get that bonus. We've had emissions reduction as part of our bonus program since 2015. ... This year we included greenhouse gas intensity metrics. If our greenhouse gas intensity is not going down, then guess what? Our employees are losing part of their bonus." And because company commitments translate into compensation, they are effective. "I absolutely believe that you need to tie company commitments to employee incentives," van Kempen said. "If you don't, then it becomes just hollow talk. You've got to put the dollar bills next to it."

Like the other elements covered in this chapter, existing incentives and commitments will both affect and be affected by your real decarbonization strategy. Employees as well as external stakeholders will consider the two interchangeable — so it's important that your efforts be entwined, consistent, and communicated well. Want to make sure your real decarbonization strategy is executed effectively? Connect today's and tomorrow's commitments and translate them into one set of targets. Successful leaders won't neglect this step. As van Kempen concluded, "What gets measured gets done."

Pull It All Together

As your team works through the critical elements of your strategy, as laid out in the upcoming chapters, you will bump against historic limitations: the way your company has always done business. Whether it's the risk calculus or misalignment of incentives, this chapter's "Take Stock" exercise is a critical step for your further work.

The team that conducts this assessment may then articulate a coherent story about where your company is today, with its strengths, weaknesses, resources, and possible blind spots. Build the company history into this starting point, to honor the experience of long-term employees and the base business that will make evolution possible. No interviewee spoke to me with more passion about the importance of acknowledging and honoring of your company's foundation and narrative than Jackson of Xcel Energy:

> *Employees talk about: "My grandpa worked at this plant."*
> *That is core to who we are and what we deliver. As we move*
> *forward through time, it's a great foundation to have, and*

that's why that respect for history is also important as we continue to look forward. What does the transition look like, and how does that continue? Because you want to carry that kind of culture forward. As we go through the transition, it's going to be a continued connection to our history, culture, and community.

Build your story into your assessment. In addition to a shared, articulated appraisal of your starting point, you can build trust and rapport by also honoring your company's past. Your real decarbonization work will be possible only because of the company's longtime employees and operations to date. Interweaving the company's past, present, and future will give company employees and stakeholders an opportunity to participate in the transition strategy, rather than feel left behind or sidelined.

Once your team has a clear-eyed understanding of where your company has been and what you have to work with, it should communicate this starting point explicitly to company leadership. This will be harder than you think. Have a discussion and duke it out. A consensus among leadership on the starting point of your company is not a given! You may have to gather more information and iterate, even here. Keep working until you have a shared understanding of where your company will begin its real decarbonization journey. Articulating the "Here's where we are" before the "Here's where we are going" allows the "why" and "how" to build on your strong foundation.

CHAPTER 4

Set the Course

Knowing where to take your decarbonization aspiration is the single most challenging component of building your real decarbonization strategy. Even for companies that have publicly committed to a target, determining whether the entire course of the company's future is compatible with that goal is a significant endeavor.

There are a few things of which you can be certain: Progress will be incremental, your plan will alienate some of your stakeholders, and there will be course corrections. This chapter explores the components of setting your company's course for its real decarbonization strategy.

The Components

Each real decarbonization strategy will be unique, and yet they will all reliably contain certain components:

- **Emissions reductions.** Companies will have to demonstrate their ability to reduce emissions in their existing operations. Annual reporting will require a well-articulated and defined baseline, short- and long-term targets for reduction, results, and plans to realize and maximize reductions.
- **Net-carbon-zero or carbon-negative plans.** Each company will lay out its pathway to net zero in Scope 1 and 2 emissions. Some companies will tackle components of Scope 3 as well. Aspirations will need to be tied to action, even where the path is foggy: Companies will need to invest in research and partnerships that show promise to fill in the gaps.
- **Investments in new technologies.** Modernizing operations — whether focused on efficiencies or an entirely new business line — will require a program for evaluating and investing in technologies new to the business or even new to the industry.
- **Evaluation of new business areas.** Companies seeking to evolve into low- and no-carbon businesses will identify their processes for assessing the risk and compatibility of new business lines with core operations.
- **Time frame and scope.** The real decarbonization strategy will have to be tied to a time frame (such as 10 years) and to clarify the scope under consideration, both geographic and in terms of business lines.

Toby Rice of EQT built all of these components into his "Unleash U.S. LNG" strategy. He told me: "I think the reason why this really resonates with people is because we're not saying for us to achieve our higher purpose, we need to stop being who we are and stop doing what we're doing. In fact, I think oil and gas companies need to be doing way more. And we have the potential to do a lot more." Rice went on to describe the imperative to address methane emissions, the expectations for net-zero Scope 1 and 2 emissions, the work necessary to build a "hydrogen-ready" grid, and the likelihood that gas infrastructure will ultimately be zero-emissions gas infrastructure. Rice tied these components directly to his strategy, with numbers and urgency. Then he conveyed this plan to his employees, in motivating terms. "That's the opportunity in front of us," he told me. "And if we do that, then we're not just digging holes in the ground to make a profit. That's not what we're about. We really are making the world a better place."

But your strategy doesn't need to include all the components. Granville Martin, head of Americas policy and outreach for the Value Reporting Foundation, formerly known as Sustainability Accounting Standards Board (SASB), homed in on finding unique company value propositions. He told me: "I think the biggest issue that companies are missing right now is the really large and growing opportunity to compete on carbon intensity of production." Martin acknowledged that capitalizing on this opportunity requires strategic course corrections. "There are some governance and intellectual changes that need to happen," he said, "for companies to seize the opportunity that's in front of them."

The rest of this chapter lays out additional factors your team will want to take into account in its direction setting. As you bear in mind the components I've laid out above, also make sure you explicitly consider your *process* for setting the course. Use this process to garner buy-in and affirm your decisions before building out the real decarbonization strategy itself.

It Will Be Iterative

"It is impossible to only have good ideas," Maynard Holt of Veriten told me during our interview. "Leaders have to show they are willing to throw out what might be a bad idea and get feedback on it to get other people to throw out their ideas." That's how Holt keeps his team from getting stuck in a rut. Encouraging broad participation works even better when applied to course setting!

Inevitably, the process of direction setting will be iterative. In fact, you'll get pretty far down your path before attaining clarity on whether you're steering the correct course. As a leader, your job is to solicit a range of ideas and ensure there is enough room to look at the dumb, the dubious, *and* the delightful. Start with a small group of trusted strategic thinkers to establish your approach. This work will be informed by the assessment you do, as outlined in Chapter 3. Work through this chapter and sketch out an 80 percent starting vision.

Then decide how much you want to work privately versus publicly while fine-tuning your direction. Two international oil and gas majors whose leaders I interviewed represented opposite ends of the strategy on whether to share the course-setting effort publicly. For example, bp, in early 2020, laid out a big, broad vision for its real decarbonization work, promising to come back with more details later in the year. Dominic Emery explained bp's process to me: "We developed a sufficiently robust strategy and supporting financials to give us confidence to lay out our purpose, our net-zero ambition, and a set of 10 aims to support that ambition [in January]. And then we said we would come back in August and September of that year and lay out the strategy and financials in more detail, which is exactly what we did."

On the opposite end of the spectrum was ExxonMobil, which mapped out detailed roadmaps on emissions reductions plans for every facility before coming out with even an emissions reduction target. Here's what Exxon's Matt Kolesar told me: "We weren't other companies. Our peer companies had made these announcements around net zero and strong greenhouse gas reductions earlier than we did, but we were always working on it." ExxonMobil required a different approach because its leadership wanted to know all the details — the "how" — before taking its plans public. "It was very important for us from a culture standpoint to have a strong sense of exactly how we were going to meet our goals," Kolesar added. "And so we've talked about developing roadmaps for every single asset that we own globally."

I've encountered this tendency frequently in my work with executive teams: Many leaders are not willing to put out goals, aspirational or tactical, that they cannot "show their work" on (to take you back to your calculus midterm days). After all, oil and gas companies are run by engineers! As Emery of bp put it, "for most engineering companies, you don't want 80:20. You'd want 100 percent. ... But to deliver that level of certainty would be impossible, even with well-understood oil and gas business models, let alone new business models for the energy transition."

"The rear view is increasingly limited in its ability to predict the future," Paula Gant of GTI Energy told me, "and that means we have a continual need to experiment and adjust, to enable an evolutionary advantage for the organization." So your company's level of planning and communication will depend on both the scope of its ambition and its comfort with communicating ambiguity. And you and other company leaders will need to sketch out a scope of effort, time frame, and end goals internally so as to have a starting point for planning, evaluation, and internal communication.

Then the iterative work can begin.

Small Bite or Big Vision?

Rice of EQT started our conversation with an interesting tidbit: "I saw an article the other day: In the U.K. they are going to feed their kids mealworms for lunch in a hope to help address climate and the emissions associated with agriculture," he told me. "I said, 'Man, these are the type of extreme solutions that people are proposing.' And I say, 'Hey, let's give these kids chicken nuggets and some LNG and we'll have an even bigger impact on the environment.'"

Your company will have to decide how big a bite it wants to take in this work. (No mealworms required!) As I laid out in Chapter 3, you will have to decide the broad trajectory within which your company plans to operate. Those trajectories again:

1. Produce and provide the last, cheapest oil and gas.
2. Create the lowest-carbon oil and gas resource.
3. Diversify the business.
4. Build a new energy company.

Then consider the time frame and ambition you want to take on. The scope and scale will be driven by the drivers discussed in Chapter 2 and the assessment described in Chapter 3.

To ascertain how big a bite, the first question to ask is: What is the role of today's base business? Alan Armstrong of Williams explained to me: "Having confidence in the value of your own base business gives you the latitude to think in the very long term." Whether the base business is responsible for generating the revenue for you to explore new ventures, reduce emissions to net zero, or slowly transition to decarbonized operations will inform the speed and scale of the company's direction.

The next question is: How ambitious does your company need to be and on what timescale? The answers to this question will change depending on the relevant external drivers, your company's change culture, and the risk appetite of your organization. One interviewee described this work on an economy-wide scale as "complicated, messy, and hard." His description applies to company work as well: "Anyone who pretends that they have a clear line of sight … to the end point of a net-zero economy clearly isn't thinking deeply enough about the problems that we face."

Finally: What are the component pieces of your ambition? Returning to the top of this chapter provides the high-level menu: There may be elements of improving efficiency and financial performance of base business operations, exploring new technologies, or evaluating novel investments. These component pieces and their relative scale will inform your company strategy.

Build a starting point — mealworm to *Dune* sandworm. The choice is yours.

The Investments

There will be a tension between today's company infrastructure and future infrastructure needs. Alice Jackson of Xcel Energy explained: "You have to continuously look at the existing facilities equipment that you have and have that mindset of continuous improvement, on 'How am I going to get more out of that equipment?' How do you make sure that it's also going to be 'hardened' — for lack of a better term — for the new situations that you're facing, at the same time [you're] looking at the uncertainties that may come in from new technologies? And how do you test those? How do you evaluate those? How do you collaborate with others and expand your horizon on who you're bringing in to have those conversations with?"

As companies explore their opportunities for action in new spaces, investments may allow them to

- Improve the base business, by promoting operational efficiency, cost saving, smaller footprint, and reduced emissions.
- Put in place new, experimental technologies that may improve the base business.
- Explore conversion or adjacent skill sets, such as converting drilling programs into carbon sequestration or geothermal, and mixing or repurposing natural gas infrastructure with hydrogen.
- Join R&D or related consortia — companies are developing research collaborations for everything from methane emissions reductions to hydrogen technology.
- Enter into venture capital partnerships — companies have either set up funds or developed partnerships both to

evaluate direct investment and to pilot the partnerships' preferred technologies within their operations.

- Implement demonstration projects — companies are teaming up with new tech companies in both traditional and new energy spaces to build pilot projects.
- Expand into new energy spaces — companies that want to diversify their base businesses may invest in anything from offshore wind to electric vehicle charging stations to demonstrate their move away from their core business.

Here's an interesting example from Jackson of building off a base business in a way that creates a win-win for the company and customers:

> [The] EVRAZ steel mill [in Pueblo, Colorado] is the steel mill that has built the Western U.S. rail system. It has over 100 years of history. And we've been connected to that facility since at least the early '70s, when they moved over to an electric arc furnace. They came to the state, and they came to us a number of years ago and said, "We either have a huge expansion coming or we might have to make our steel elsewhere." And so we got creative on looking at how could we help stabilize and have a known cost for this customer for electricity, because electricity is a core component of their production. And so we sat down at a table, and we brainstormed on options, and ultimately came to an outcome where we have now helped them construct the largest behind-the-meter solar generation facility—almost 300 megawatts. It's huge! That's a utility-sized system for a single customer that also supports the system and provides benefits for the rest of the customers in the state. So it not only kept the company here, it enabled them to expand. We partnered closely with the community and with the customer to get to success. And we found a way to make them the greenest steel mill in the world.

Creative brainstorms, unconventional partnerships, new investments, novel collaborations — these are options for investment as your company explores its real decarbonization strategy. Consider what is palatable to company culture to understand the menu of options at your disposal. You'll map this work out in Chapter 8.

Companies to Watch

Oil and gas companies rarely want to be first movers, so leaders are advised to survey the public and private activities of their peer companies. Much of the ESG and decarbonization work happening in small and midsize oil and gas companies is subterranean, meaning they are testing out ideas internally and haven't yet shared them publicly.

Therefore, prepare a list of your peer companies, your slightly bigger or more advanced competitors, and then your customer companies. Many of the pressures coming to companies will be moving up the supply chain, so you may be required to act on the basis of the expectations of your customers before those of even your investors.

There can be a lot of internal cultural barriers to getting too ambitious in a company's energy transition strategy. As Martin of the Value Reporting Foundation told me, companies will have to overcome governance norms as well as historic political expectations to take advantage of the opportunities available today.

Conversely, in my work with companies, I've noted three drivers that fast-track change: (1) peer companies' lead, (2) customers' procurement requirements (or preferences!), and (3) investors' expectations.

Keeping tabs on the activities of your peers helps you know your competitive landscape, and it also builds serious momentum within your company. Survey their ESG reporting as well as publicly made aspirational commitments. Identify two to three companies that are leading the way and reach out to one of them for a confidential conversation. By the time companies make announcements, their work may have been underway for two years or more. You can learn a lot from an off-the-record discussion.

You may find that customers and investors are willing to be incredibly transparent about what they need from your company and why. After all, they are facing the same ever-changing landscape of pressures — and if you succeed, you help them win as well.

Who Should Decide?

Even in the face of so much external pressure, companies crafting a comprehensive ESG and decarbonization vision will face strong blowback. External stakeholders will doubt your sincerity, long-time employees may think you've sold out, and board directors may wonder if you've lost your way. Again and again, interviewees stated that the company CEO must have the courage and commitment to carry a vision and its inherent value proposition convincingly to all stakeholders.

Which isn't to say that CEO commitment is enough. It isn't. Wise CEOs consult on their plans with trusted partners, widening the circle of input and communication until participation in the vision is broad. We will revisit the importance of this buy-in and collaboration in Chapters 5 and 6.

Read the Rest of This Book Before You Get Started

Iteration is going to be such an important part of setting your company's strategy that I recommend reading the rest of this book before you get too far. Early consideration of company culture, incentives, organization structure, and financial investment — all topics I deal with at length in subsequent chapters — will and must shape the initial direction of your strategy.

Executives that I interviewed had some cogent advice on this initial direction setting:

- **Understand the relationship between your ambition and your base business**. Vicki Hollub told me how Oxy's enhanced oil recovery experience makes it uniquely positioned for handling and sequestering carbon dioxide.
- **Don't try to look at everything.** Set some guardrails for scope. Rob Sadler described DCP Midstream's default approach this way: "We look at everything in the world that's cool, and we have 10,000 different ideas and concepts and things that are amazingly interesting, and none of them are executable, and none of them make financial sense." Always apply relentlessly stringent criteria — guardrails — to what you will focus on, he recommended. "The focus is, we've got to build new technical capabilities, but we also are in a business to run a business and to make money," he explained.
- **Factor in your company's risk and ambiguity tolerance.** Hollub explained that new business arenas are going to require new financial instruments and a new risk-to-ROI calculus.
- **Contemplate the interface between the old and the new.** There will be haves and have-nots, Chad Zamarin of Williams told me — adding that thinking carefully about how you will separate, bridge, or intertwine the old and the new is important.

The most difficult step in the transition strategy will be to set the course. Your course will incorporate the following elements:

- **Objectives.** Clarify what your company intends to accomplish and why.
- **Trajectory.** How big a transformation is open for consideration?

- **Aspirations and goals.** Lay out both your aspirational vision and your specific, time-dependent goals. A good transition strategy will incorporate elements of both, which will evolve over time.

- **Components.** Will you look at everything from emissions reductions to new business?

- **Tie in to your strategic plan.** Your transition strategy must be clearly interwoven and aligned with your company's other plans and goals — either serving as a subpart or taking a central role. In addition to strategic, operational, and financial plans, the transition strategy must be explicitly aligned with ESG aspirations, goals, and reporting.

- **Plan for iterations and revisions.** It is certain that your initial course will involve unanticipated challenges. If your team is damn lucky, it may also include miraculous alignment with the desires of your internal and external stakeholders. In either case, the approach will require multiple revisions. Rather than counting on your teams to make decisions on the fly, lay out the expectations and time frames for revisiting the course as you develop your real decarbonization strategy.

CHAPTER 5

Critical Element 1: Your People

In my first outline of this book, I thought the driving "critical element" was going to be "structure"; however, my interviews with executives made clear that the buy-in and participation of the company's workforce will sink or float any energy transition effort. So, although the "people element" of your transition is not the first part that you will work on in your strategy, it is so important to your effort that it requires your up-front consideration before you can take on the external engagement, structural, and innovation elements.

As Chad Zamarin of Williams described, energy transition work is about the convergence of "leadership and opportunity." This convergence works only if ideas and participation are flowing across company silos and throughout the hierarchy. He went on to describe an effort beyond creating something new; when talking about Williams's New Energy Ventures team, he described its mission as "to figure out how to evolve the DNA of the entire organization" and "to figure out how to make the next generation of opportunities a part of our core business." Such an effort requires a rethinking of company culture, individuals' characteristics and skill sets, and company communications and incentives. That's what this chapter is about, as Zamarin concluded: "untapping the full potential of the organization."

Characteristics and Skill Sets

The most common question I get from employees is "What skill sets should I be building today to ensure I'm a company leader as the oil and gas industry changes?" I posed that question to company leaders, anticipating that there would be one skill set for rising leaders and others for individual contributors, but instead, I found that there is no one set of competencies needed to achieve upward mobility; in an energy transition, there are multiple paths to leadership that transcend traditional management hierarchy. In this chapter I will look at the roles employees can fill and the characteristics and skill sets that they will require.

Companies will need to bridge the existing, traditional skill sets and the needs of an innovative workplace culture. Brian Schettler is head of AEI HorizonX, a venture capital collaboration with Boeing. He emphasized the importance of creating connective tissue between the experienced employees and the new ideas coming in. Schettler told me, "You want your engineers to have confidence; you want your engineers to be proud of the work that they're doing. But it's getting the balance just right … bridging new forms of innovation with inside expertise."

The Doer in All of Us

Dominic Emery of bp went to pains to emphasize the importance of the workers who carry out the many operational functions of an organization. A leader, he said, "must have a workforce of technical and professional qualifications: great engineers, geoscientists, commercial people, great deal-doers." Alice Jackson of Xcel Energy described the ideal workforce this way: "You need a series of problem-solvers who also respect the history that comes to the table."

And even the basic expectations of the workforce have changed. Leaders described qualities required of all employees in the current era:

- **Empathy.** Because oil and gas work is by its nature cooperative, across functions and across stakeholder groups, the ability to imagine another's perspective is an essential characteristic for employees.

- **Adaptability.** The rate of technological, social, and political change ensures that having the capacity to evolve is important for employees' ability to contribute to existing and new business areas.

- **Curiosity.** I have observed in my work that the secret ingredient for pivoting from *resisting change* to *embracing change* is curiosity. Curiosity looks at a disruption as something to be understood, learned from — and even leveraged as an opportunity.

- **Political savvy.** So much of getting projects done in today's environment requires the ability to navigate a complex mix of regulations, policy, and stakeholder expectations. As Alan Armstrong of Williams stated, "Now you don't just need technical solutions, but politically palatable solutions that bring along stakeholders." A company's technical expertise is irrelevant if it can't get a permit.

- **Cooperation.** The need for cooperation is obvious, but as Emery explained, it has been elevated with the changing nature of our work: "The nature of the business that we're seeking to do now relies very much on high-quality partnerships: being able to choose those partnerships and then being able to work collaboratively toward a common goal." Both internally and externally, cooperation can be leveraged to transcend isolation, bridge differences, and find win-win solutions.

Interestingly, these qualities do not need to be inherent. Employees and managers can explicitly cultivate them, seeking to build up new capabilities to meet the challenges entailed by their companies' real decarbonization strategy.

Making a Place for the Old Guard

There are expected battles between an oil and gas company's legacy workforce and its new recruits. Yet over and over I heard stories from company leaders of its being precisely their old guard who praised the company pivot. "I'm of a certain age," one executive was told, "but what you're doing for my grandkids is just fantastic." Another said, "I feel almost personally responsible for a million tons of CO_2." And that employee asked to work on CCS as a way to take part in the transition.

More experienced oil and gas employees throughout the organization play important roles beyond their day-to-day job excellence. The old guard also

- Know how to navigate company processes to get things done.
- Have the most practical knowledge of areas for operational improvement.
- Can translate aspiration into practical action within company culture, procedures, and operations.

Xcel's Jackson conveys the tension between the traditional businesses and the energy transition as she recounts this interaction with an employee at a coal-fired power plant:

> One gentleman came up to me at the end of our Legislative
> Day event, and he said, "You know what? I'm so proud of

what our company is doing. We're doing the right thing on leading the clean energy transition." He continued, "I'm proud of what our state is doing in taking and making the hard decisions on moving this forward. I just have one question: How am I going to feed my family?" So it goes back to that emotional side of the transition and the choices that we're making. But he's fully supportive. And he had ideas for me that he went into after that, on how can we help the community ... make progress. He'd read about technologies and had all kinds of questions. I get asked about everything from nuclear to battery storage to new hydro technologies to geothermal. It is our employees who bring those ideas and ways of executing forward.

Schettler of AEI HorizonX described how he interfaces between traditional Boeing employees and those within the start-up ventures: "The key to success is to create a dedicated team within the big company to help bridge the new thinking and technology with the history and expertise that come from your internal innovators. You have to build a concrete program that gets the new technology exposed to business units and technology leaders while also providing a mechanism to be creative on how to apply the new tech to in-house needs and gaps."

The Up-and-Comer

Oil and gas companies have their cadre of upwardly mobile leaders, with a twist: These leaders have come up through the traditional oil and gas ranks and yet are preparing for an inevitably disrupted future. They are keenly attuned to upcoming challenges, from digitalization to decarbonization. As Wouter van Kempen of DCP Midstream told me, the table stakes for these leaders are the same as they've always been: "You'd better get results. And a promise made is a promise kept." What is new is that these leaders must "look over the horizon and be able to pivot really, really quickly." And then they must be able to manage through all that change.

Dan Harple, founder and CEO of Context Labs, described these up-and-comers as "the evangelists." These are the forward-looking idea people who have the respect and gravitas to sell their ideas up. A lot of real decarbonization strategy comes from motivated people within the company willing to evangelize for positive change.

Furthermore, the leaders of tomorrow will have to be collaborative. As Armstrong of Williams told me, "People that are really comfortable taking time to explain the why, not because 'I said so' but because 'We need to do this, and here's how we need your help,' are really engaging people's passion and energy around helping to solve problems."

The Navigator

The bridge builders between the old and new guards will be experienced company employees who decide to help integrate new recruits and new functions within company operations. Zamarin of Williams calls them the "navigators." They will translate for new employees, telling them how things actually get done within the confines of existing operations and bureaucracy. Bridge builders will have an interest in the energy transition and feel ownership in its success, while recognizing that they may not be directly contributing to all the shiny new activities. Company leaders will need to not only cultivate navigators but also incentivize their success.

The Outsider

Companies will inevitably have to bring in outside talent to fill experience gaps in their transition plans. An increasingly digitalized and tech-focused world requires this influx. The key lesson oil and gas leaders offered is to pair newcomers, especially in senior positions, with navigators to help them get their work done. Leaders learned that any kind of "burn it down" mentality is doomed to fail. Therefore, not only deliberate exploration for but also intentional integration of external leaders is very important.

Magic in a Bottle

Energy transition leaders are looking to cultivate a mix of skill sets and characteristics on their leadership team. Schettler described the kind of leaders he is looking for: "You want to start with an executive who has an open mind, is embracing change, isn't fearful of change, and isn't hardwired to be so risk-averse that you'll never get any kind of progress."

For you, the individual, I like what Zamarin described as the qualities to cultivate in yourself. He's looking for a balance between the right-brained creativity and curiosity and the left-brained focus on rigor and results. As he says, "Those don't always naturally show up together." But when they do, it's "magic in a bottle."

So as an individual and as a manager, you can consciously curate that mix of capabilities both within yourself and within your team. And as an individual and as a team leader, you need to strive for results with rigor, yet combine that rigor with creativity and curiosity. As one leader concluded, "What are we trying to create? An empowered workforce interested in evolving as individuals and a collective."

Communications, Training, and Incentives

Some best practices emerged from companies' experiences with building their transition strategies. To put your people first in your energy transition strategy, consider these actions:

- **Listening tour.** Leaders who conducted listening tours of company operations received much higher levels of buy-in among staff. It's worth considering a listening tour early in your planning process, much like an ESG materiality assessment. This gives you an understanding, as part of your strategic planning, of what cultural hurdles and motivational opportunities you face. Throughout rollout and execution, planned listening sessions across operations and locations create opportunities for employees to air grievances and for you to gather improvement ideas.

- **Communicating the strategy.** The reality among most oil and gas companies is that it is very experienced, senior leadership driving the energy transition effort, with significant support from the millennial and Gen Z workforce. Your company must develop a "change story" that ties the role of the middle manager into executing your vision on the ground. The vision includes the drivers, the aspiration, the strategy, and the role of employees in its execution. We'll take on the change story in Chapter 9.
- **Training.** One of the biggest grievances of change strategies is a perception of haves and have-nots. This attitude can apply to the allotment of resources for operational priorities; it often is grounded in fear of being left behind. You as a company leader need to address this fear by creating training opportunities focusing on "skills of the future" across the workforce.
- **The hybrid reality.** All of this change management is happening in an unusual context: a hybrid workspace. Your communications and listening tour strategy must accommodate the reality of a workforce that is rarely together, and in which numerous employees have spent more time working from home than with their colleagues.

Space for Disagreement

Because energy transition work is caught up in political polarization, company leaders must contend with the pushback that they will get, from both generic resistance to change and individual entrenchment in political identity. Company leaders I work with have addressed this in myriad ways, but they all had one theme: Create a public place for employees to express their skepticism.

Not every leader is on board out of the gate with creating a space for disagreement. "Why would I open that can of worms?" is a common refrain! Yet the leaders who are leading companies through their real decarbonization have a strong commitment to — even a strong interest in — airing opposition to their ideas. This should not be confused with spending too much time with, as one leader put it, the "20 percent": "There's 20 percent of the people who truly, truly hate and dislike change and will railroad it."

The other reason to cultivate constructive disagreement is to learn from employees and improve the process. Harple told me, "I least respect the people who acquiesce to me, and I love the people who are resolved enough to actually engage in advancing dialogue. Because I love the co-invention of stuff. It's like if you play tennis with someone better than you, you're always going to get better. So I'm always looking for people to do that with each other."

As leaders express their genuine passion for the work ahead, employees will find their own connections to the change story of the company. That means they explore and challenge their own thinking and assumptions. You can make a space for this by encouraging your employees to contribute to the narrative: What needs to be done? Where can they contribute? What am I missing? How can we do this better?

Grievances will be aired. Whether publicly or privately is up to the process your company puts in place to channel them. When captured and channeled, those criticisms will make your real decarbonization strategy better.

The Why

And I'll close this chapter on the most critical element, your people, with a little inspiration from Wiliams's Armstrong: "What was somewhat unexpected on my part was the amount of people power that we've gotten out of this — the amount of passion, and energy, and excitement that we've gotten, particularly out of our millennials — and how enthused they are to work for a company that they feel is leading on this issue. And, you know, if you can get that kind of connection and passion for the company you just get more and more out of people, and they like their jobs better."

The uptake and success of company strategy is entirely dependent on the participation of the employee base. Armstrong's philosophy: "I'm a big believer that the difference between a great company and a mediocre company is the passion and energy you get out of people in your organization."

Once your real decarbonization strategy is underway, its communication and execution will require the inclusion of participants across operations, divisions, branches, and levels. The input and buy-in will require broad engagement. Taking a clear-eyed look at your company culture as it is today and considering what is required will pave the way for the work ahead.

C H A P T E R   6

Critical Element 2: Your Community of Stakeholders

"Leadership ... is not about organizations. It is not about plans. It is not about strategies. It is all about people — motivating people to get the job done. You have to be people-centered."

— Colin Powell

Every single component of your company's real decarbonization strategy needs to be about people. A lot of this book is about the people *within* the company — but in this chapter, we explore the people *outside* the company and how they can, should, or will inform this critical new strategy. I'm not talking a check-the-box stakeholder engagement approach — that would be easy, but also predictable and not particularly helpful. Instead, let's imagine how a company that is re-inventing itself on a multi-decade timeline can think about all the people outside of the company who will absorb, inform, change, and be changed by the work ahead.

You can be the informer and disruptor of the energy transition — or you can be the guy who fell into the energy future pool fully dressed at the company picnic and spent the rest of the evening trying to figure out what happened. The

63

difference between those two options comes down to your level of decisive engagement with your community of stakeholders — both informing them and being informed by them.

Engaging with your community of stakeholders is not for the faint of heart. Because when I say "engaging them," I am not talking about "educating them." You are meeting your stakeholders on level ground, as peers.

To lead into the energy future — as opposed to falling into the energy future backward — oil and gas leaders must have both have a sense of urgency and an enduring patience. On the one hand, you face pressing demands to transform your business in response to changing societal needs and stakeholder expectations. On the other, you'll need to engage those stakeholders on their terms and in their language. You'll engage with them because (1) you will co-create your strategy with them, (2) your relationship with them will inform their experience and knowledge of the energy transition, and (3) this is the only route to building a shared understanding of the important role of oil and gas companies in the energy transition.

A Permeable Strategy

As a result, your real decarbonization strategy is permeable. Correction: An *ultimately successful* real decarbonization strategy is permeable. (Plenty of energy transition strategies are rigid and out of date before the ink is dry.) By "permeable," I mean that the strategy serves as a living wall for the cell that is the company — a flexible, stretchy, and porous membrane that allows the organism to grow and absorb information optimally. That's because real decarbonization:

- Must adapt to the circumstances ahead, including technological breakthroughs, customer preferences, regulatory updates, and financial realities.
- Will be informed by the preferences of many customers and consumers, which will change frequently.

- Can itself influence both the circumstances and preferences ahead through its innovation, outreach, and operational performance.

Many of the executives I interviewed talked about the accelerating pace of disruption they and their companies are encountering now and the increasing violence of the disruptions. Successful real decarbonization leaders are finding opportunity in these constant disruptions for their own, positive disruptions — of their business models and their approaches to shareholder, community, and customer relations. Here we focus on how we can create and influence those positive disruptions through our transition strategies.

That disruption work, insists Toby Rice of EQT, is really stakeholder work. "From a leadership perspective, it's not just about digging a hole in the ground and making money," he told me. "Our work is really about stakeholders. It's landowners. It's the environment; Mother Earth is a stakeholder! And we've got to be compassionate about the concerns that a lot of people have." Rice acknowledges that achieving that level of compassion and attention is no easy feat: "That's the hard part as a leader," he told me. "The bigger your company gets, the more stakeholders you need to satisfy. … And that is where you need to have values, and you need to be clear about your mission and your higher purpose."

Engendering trust in those stakeholders — especially the skeptical ones — is key, said Dan Harple of Context Labs. Harple and his team achieve it by declaring that "the situation is the boss" and working with potential antagonists to satisfy the needs of the energy transition situation — in Context Labs' case, by creating trusted, transparent, verifiable data. "The industry needs trusted data to accelerate the energy transition," he told me.

Six Fronts

So how does this permeable membrane of a strategy yield opportunities for your company — opportunities to explicitly craft your interactions with a world that expects it to *both transform and be transformed* on its way to the energy future? Let's look at six fronts — fronts where your company meets the external world. It is on these fronts where you will both proactively encounter disruptions and have the opportunity to engage constructively with your stakeholders.

Values and Culture

Your company's values and culture must evolve along with its real decarbonization strategy. To build trust internally and externally, company leaders must foster values and a culture that acknowledge the company's impact — positive and negative, disruptive and stabilizing, traditional and innovative — on your greater stakeholder community. In this way, your values and company culture can authentically inform your stakeholder interactions to propagate good and minimize harm.

When I asked Martha Hall Findlay, the chief climate officer of Suncor, about the leadership qualities she thought were required for real decarbonization, she stressed the nature of leaders' relationships with their employees and key outside stakeholders first. "Trust and performance," Hall Findlay told me. "You can't lead unless your team and potential collaborators trust you. You can't effectively lead unless you trust your team. And performance is key to building trust." These are the base conditions that allow companies to go out and engage, building trust within stakeholder communities.

"It's a balancing act for sure," explained Shantanu Agarwal, co-founder and president of Susteon, a decarbonization R&D start-up. "We have to solve these little problems. At the same time, the big picture is key to make sure you are moving in the right direction. It all boils down to the team." Over and over I heard similar responses — that executives leading real decarbonization work are wise to cultivate and curate the values and culture behind the team. A strong company culture provides the base from which stakeholder relationships are formed.

Workforce

Your frontline employees are the living embodiment of your company's integration into its communities — and that's why those employees are crucial to the success of your real decarbonization strategy. "Our employees are out there in the middle of snowstorms, rainstorms, bomb cyclones, polar vortexes," Alice Jackson of Xcel Energy told me, "all to make sure that our customers and our communities can thrive and move forward. ... As we go through the transition, our work will involve continued connection to community."

Your company's workforce is also, in its own way, permeable with the broader community. You hire your teams from the broader community, and they go home from work to it, volunteer in it, spend their weekends with it, and retire back into it. Your employees represent their community to your company and represent your company to their community — and thinking about your workforce in those ways puts their participation in and buy-in to your real decarbonization strategy front and center.

An important key to workforce-community success: having a diverse workforce and an equitable and inclusive company culture. Anthony Oni has a utility background, founded a clean-tech start-up called Cloverly, and now works in venture capital for clean-energy start-ups as managing partner and chief executive officer at Energy Impact Partners' (EIP) Elevate Future Fund. He conveyed to me during our interview the importance of building connective tissue between the workforce and stakeholder community. "We open an aperture wider," he said of this dynamic. "When you allow more people to come in, they incorporate their lived experiences into solving some of these problems."

Critics and Partners

Unconventional engagements and alliances are becoming the norm for oil and gas companies — and they must be part of your strategy as well. Onetime critics such as shareholder activists are now frequently partners in shaping the compromises that keep shareholder initiatives off the proxy ballot. Hall Findlay of Suncor advised: "Be proactive, because it speaks to generating trust; it speaks to action and performance. Instead of waiting for someone to tell you what to do or regulate you potentially out of business, take action before you need either the carrot or the stick." The expectation to engage with labor, community groups, eNGOs, think tanks, and academics will only grow — and your company will be wise to set aside leadership time and resources to shape and participate meaningfully in such engagements.

EQT's Rice crafted his "Unleash U.S. LNG" strategy from this unconventional-engagements premise. "If we want to continue to do the great work that we do, we need to address the concerns about climate," he told me. "We're not taking an approach where we're going to try and convince people that they should not be concerned about climate; that's not our argument. Other people can have that debate. Our angle is 'Can we step back and look at some things that we can do to help address people's concerns over climate?'"

Maynard Holt of Veriten told me he believes that this larger engagement is critical not only to company success but to employee ownership of real decarbonization work. "Employees will not offer ideas if they don't feel trusted, cared about, and part of a bigger mission," he said. "When people feel that there is a mission that is bigger than their job, then they will do something extraordinary."

I've engaged in many collaborations across eNGOs and industry, and here's what I've learned: Most participants start with an expectation that they are going to teach the other party about something they value. In a great engagement, what actually happens is that the parties each come away with a broader perspective on the problem: It's more complex and nuanced than their previous viewpoints allowed them to see. This creates an opportunity for new conversations, which may allow for compromise, incremental change, and novel solutions.

Investors

Like your ESG engagement, your real decarbonization strategy will be both informed by and accountable to your investors and their ever-evolving expectations. Companies that regularly engage with their investors outside of quarterly calls and expected reporting will find that they can positively influence these relationships while expanding their understanding of key investor drivers.

Oni has been on both sides of the investor relationship. He told me he thinks the relationship between investment and community is "critically important, as the environment and climate change issues we face impact everyone globally. Low-income, underserved communities bear the brunt of some everyday climate and justice issues." Engaging investors in conversations about these issues allows for shared understanding as well as mutual learning and helps create positive change through the deployment of capital.

Vicki Hollub of Oxy has engaged with diverse partners, from labor unions to foreign governments to the pope — and has to come to anticipate initial partner skepticism that an oil and gas company could be interested in decarbonization. "You learn that others really care about the planet, really want to do the right thing, but just don't understand that we in the oil and gas industry can be a part of it," she told me. "We *can* be a part of the solution. And what I've learned is: We have to be patient with that message. ... It's going to take a while before people will get it."

Investors and shareholders are a diverse bunch. And they are all subject to their own influences and pressures. Engaging with investors proactively and transparently allows you to understand and address their unique and changing needs. Investors, after all, are crafting their own decarbonization strategies — whether intentionally or reactively. By working with them, you can inform, participate in, and perhaps even help accelerate their strategies.

Environmental Justice

Don't make the mistake of routinely undervaluing either the opportunities or the challenges of working with historically disadvantaged communities in your energy transition projects. All future projects — whether pipeline, traditional facility, or clean-energy hub — will require high levels of engagement with surrounding communities. This is where permeability can create mutual rewards.

For instance, look for opportunities centered on building partnerships around job creation, economic prosperity, and revitalization. Oni of the EIP Elevate Future Fund told me he's seen the advantages of working directly with communities. "Utilities have ready-made pathways for community engagement that have been used as communication points to promote growth and workforce initiatives and ensure everyone can access clean, safe, affordable, and reliable energy," he said.

The challenges to these opportunities include the inevitable opposition to new projects, especially in the absence of engagement. You can overcome these challenges by leading with a thoughtful, humble strategy. Hollub of Oxy described for me how this approach works. First, she has in place an empathetic team to start these conversations with communities: "Our team has a unique ability to put themselves in the mindset of the groups that we're interfacing with — to understand the perspectives that they're dealing with and to listen to what they view the challenges to be." The community's initial resistance, she said, can usually be overcome through deep listening. "It's by allowing yourself to be open to those who may tell you they want you to go away — having the ability to sit there and listen to that, and to understand what they really mean …" Hollub explained. "And [by beginning] to work from that concept and perspective, we can then work toward a solution that helps us both." Hollub summarized this approach: "How do we learn what we need to learn to be able to come up with the solution?"

Your company will want to explicitly articulate its EJ approach, guideposts, and engagement strategies — from macro planning to specific project implementation — throughout your real decarbonization strategy. It will be through engagement with historically disadvantaged communities that your company will have some of its biggest, most transformative impact. Your projects will be changed by your engagement with these communities, and ultimately, so will your company strategy.

Skill Sets and Training

In building your strategy, you will develop a pretty good idea of your company's blind spots and strengths when it comes to workforce experience, characteristics, and skill sets. But here's the opportunity: You can use your real decarbonization strategy to *create* the workforce of the future for your company.

You can look at this process any number of ways. For instance, Mark Brownstein of EDF emphasized leadership skills. "The leaders I most enjoy working with and who I think are the most effective are those who are intellectually curious," he told me. "Intellectually honest — with themselves, their peers, and with stakeholders. They apply the same level of rigor to environmental performance that they do to financial performance."

Think about your hiring and workforce development with your real decarbonization strategy in mind, for everything from digital skills to interpersonal engagement. How you execute your strategy—and how you must adjust it to changing conditions — should drive how you imagine and articulate your recruiting, training, and cross-training opportunities. And how you select and grow your staff determines the health of your strategy.

Put People at the Center

Everything about your real decarbonization strategy is done by, for, and with — and is accountable to — people. The strategy must make this fundamental quality clear by explicitly articulating the role of each people-centric element of the plan. Ultimately, this is an "optimistic exercise," as Dominic Emery of bp said in Chapter 3.

A real decarbonization strategy can serve to both empower your workforce and intertwine your organization with your stakeholder communities. Granville Martin of the Value Reporting Foundation observed during our interview how this interaction between company and stakeholders accelerates positive change in a company. "It's extremely hopeful that most people at operating companies are aggressive, motivated, effective, and innovative," he said. "If we get folks in public and private company communities focused on minimizing environmental impacts, we will be successful." Use your planning work to imagine, test, and articulate the ways in which you will build the communities and workforce of the future with your company's strategy.

This permeable real decarbonization strategy "membrane" will allow your company to adapt to the unknown unknowns ahead, to be informed by the ever-changing expectations of your stakeholders, and in fact to influence the ways the energy transition plays out. When you explicitly address the interconnected effects with key groups, real decarbonization work becomes the starting point for a shared journey.

Critical Element 3: Your Structure

"The only human institution which rejects progress is the cemetery."

— Harold Wilson

Company reorganizations are dreadful, hard work — for everyone. Yet working out how to translate aspirational decarbonization work into a company's structure is the best kind of dreadful, hard work — because it is so important. You won't get it exactly right the first time, so create margin for you and your team to correct course.

But let's back up a second and first carefully consider why you need to make any changes to your structure at all. As Paula Gant of GTI Energy told me, "The speed of the technology and market change overall outpaces the abilities of our top-down management structures. The insights needed to maintain competitive advantage won't be found in a small group of individuals." In the same way that your real decarbonization strategy must show a value proposition to your investors, your reorganization needs to demonstrate value to your employees. Structural changes will align incentives, enhance innovation, and demonstrate results within the organization to accommodate the strategy.

Executives repeatedly told me that they had initially overcomplicated their real decarbonization strategy around structure. On the basis of their input, I recommend you consider instead a building block method that ties planned organizational changes clearly to the course set in Chapter 4. Every change should have a "why" that has been considered for consequences, including unintended consequences. When in doubt, do less. When the planning team starts getting lost in the changes, return to simplicity. Strong leaders have to be receptive and nimble. As Scott Sheffield, chief executive officer of Pioneer Natural Resources, explained to me: "It's not 'My way or the highway.' You have to be humble and very, very open to communication."

Every element of structural change and integration for your strategy must have CEO and board buy-in. As you consider implementing changes to your organization structure, iterate with leadership and your board until you get to your best, most elegant solution with upper-level buy-in. Then stress-test it again for the value proposition to investors: Will the work empower employee buy-in, spur innovation, and drive results?

In the early days of ESG, Sheffield stepped out as a leader who embraced regulation. "You have to be confident that what you're doing is right," he told me during our interview, "and I think it's better for us to be a leader in ESG matters." Your structure will reflect the commitments you make as a leader.

An Extreme Exercise in Change Management

Wouter van Kempen related to me that he likes to ask groups of DCP Midstream employees, "Who here likes change?" Bringing up the dreaded topic explicitly creates a space to state the obvious: People don't like change *when it affects them.* (He joked that most people agree that change that affects other people is great!)

Embarking on a real decarbonization strategy is an extreme exercise in change management. Recognize that at the core of every evolution in a company — strategy, operations, organization, and investments — are employees and teams who have to process the change. Now, van Kempen is an individual who embraces change; but by his own account, his attitude is shared by probably only about 10 percent of the workforce. So company leaders must be keenly aware of how they will approach change from the perspective of company culture, the people required to evolve into new responsibilities, and the communication required to keep the change moving forward.

By van Kempen's estimation, about 20 percent of any workforce is going to resist change. In fact, he goes a step further and acknowledges that those folks will actively fight it. As you plan your strategy, it's important to be attuned to the dynamics of change embracers and change fighters to consider where they will fit in your new organization. And the other 70 percent? Those are the people van Kempen says you focus on — engaging them in the company's story of change. We'll talk about the change story in Chapter 9.

The Board

As discussed in Chapter 3, the CEO generally takes the lead in articulating the value proposition of any new energy strategy to the board of directors. On a healthy board, there will be a fair amount of give-and-take on setting the course, with some laggards arguing for the status quo and an outlier or two pushing for faster energy transition action. This will be the case on everything from modernization and digitalization to work on diversity, equity, and inclusion.

While you consider the structural changes required of your organization for real decarbonization, know that several will affect the board:

- **New expertise.** Very likely, the board will require new expertise to help guide, shape, and hold accountable your new business functions.

- **Additional governance.** Like the development of the company ESG strategy, the new energy transition endeavors will require direction and accountability to the board. You may need to consider expanding the responsibility of existing board committees, developing new, relevant committees, or assigning board members to work directly with executives with new responsibilities.
- **Reassess risk.** The calculus for investment and project returns will likely be different than in traditional business lines. The expected ROI may need to be different, as may the reasonable time frame to expect that return. In some cases, companies are seeking a low-percentage, high-impact return. Your board should be explicitly engaged in calibrating the acceptable financial risk.
- **Evolve decision-making criteria.** Companies undergoing their energy transition work quickly require a framework and process for choosing what to invest in. As we'll review further in Chapter 7, there are a number of reasonable approaches to structuring your investment decisions. A key step is gaining board input and buy-in to the criteria and process, as well as determining where final decision-making authority will lie.

The New Leadership

Across the companies I interviewed, new executive leadership positions have been created. Ideally, such new positions report to the CEO. Van Kempen explained to me why new executive leadership must have a direct line to the top: "If something is important to you as a company, it had better be important to you as the CEO."

If you're like me, you might expect leaders of new ventures groups to come most often from outside the company. In reality, a majority of these leaders have been internally promoted. Appointing a strong operational leader into a new position serves two purposes: (1) It conveys across the organization that the new function is central to company direction, and (2) it allows the new leader to build pragmatic bridges between the new, creative — and often unrealistic — ideas of the new business area and the practical realities of executing within the organization.

These leaders do often bring in outside talent. Oil and gas leaders know how difficult it can be to recruit from outside the industry, especially over the past five years, when the industry has been caricatured as energy of the past (and the villain on climate). But company leaders I spoke with were surprised at how easy it had been to bring in outside talent once they had articulated their real decarbonization strategies. Such strategies say, "Hey, look — you can be a part of a meaningful historic enterprise and craft the future!"

Promoting known, talented company leaders sends a signal from the top. The leaders can then bring outside experience, ideas, and skills into your real decarbonization plans. This infusion of talent and perspectives sets up your team to navigate between the old and the new — one of the most challenging tasks ahead.

Organizational Structure

The organizational structure for your energy transition will, naturally, be highly dependent on your company's current state and course. Regardless of those variables, however, the structure must enable action and drive results. Vicki Hollub of Oxy described one of her priorities in making results happen through structure: "One of the changes has to be that we empower our employees to make decisions quicker and make decisions that are within their area of expertise and focus." Consider what reforms you need to make to drive organizational changes that will underpin the hard work of real decarbonization execution.

Temporal nature. Some elements will be transitory in nature and may require explicitly temporary roles. For example, a chief transformation officer might have a two-year window to enact change. A vice president of energy transitions might have an open-ended runway. An "innovations team" could be given a one-year mandate, leaving the opportunity to build out a new business line at the end of the year. Van Kempen put it succinctly to me: "If you have a chief transformation officer role for 20 years, I don't think you're very transformative, correct?" Consider the elements required and what message the time frame conveys about the strategy.

Existing and needed skill sets. In addition to the characteristics of the workforce I discussed in Chapter 5, your departments and teams may have translatable skills that can be stretched, strengthened, or repurposed. Similarly, some gaps may be readily apparent. Identify needs, existing resources, and gaps as you think about how to structure a mix of experienced teams with new recruits.

Evolve the rotation. Oil and gas companies routinely rotate high-performance employees through different company departments and locations. Building in new business areas or functions requires an evolution in thinking about the rotation. Some new company recruits may not be suited to such a rotation — or, alternatively, they may benefit enormously from exposure to the realities of existing operations. Think carefully about how to use this time-honored tradition in innovative ways to benefit your real decarbonization strategy.

Today. Tomorrow. Simplify. Without undue deference to what exists today, map out an organizational chart that supports existing operations, makes new spaces for what's required in the strategy, and considers the structural bridges between them. Spend some time exploring what an elegant, straightforward structure could look like. Resist the urge to make it too complex or to solve for too many intricacies. You'll need to iterate dozens of times as you work through the elements of your strategy. Keep simplifying.

New roles. A good criterion for creating new roles is "Does someone need to wake up thinking about this?" As Rob Sadler of DCP Midstream put it to me, "You can't be successful with energy transition, sustainability, or any kind of major initiative if it's just a hobby." Your company will need to create new roles when the work will require full-time attention. These roles can have a planned shelf life or be open-ended, as the situation dictates.

Plan to iterate. As you reorganize, build expectation for change and flexibility into the new structure. Chad Zamarin of Williams said he tells team members, "We're going to try things; we're going to keep evolving as we figure things out." Companies a few years ahead on real decarbonization tend to describe their evolution as 1.0, 2.0, and so on, with the expectation that iteration is built into the strategy. Because real decarbonization is charting new territory, building course corrections into your planning will allow you to both manage expectations and make the most of what you learn along the way.

Managing Today Versus Tomorrow

"This is a hard job," summarized UCSD researcher David Victor of the tasks ahead for those tackling real decarbonization while maintaining their current core businesses. "[If] you're running an incumbent firm, you've got to do both. You've got to run your current core business and plan that core business for an uncertain but highly probable future." That balance between the commitments of today and the "highly probably future" of tomorrow is central to the architecture of your structure.

As if all that weren't complicated enough, Victor reminded me, there are even more variables to account for. "The speed of the transition is unknowable, but you've got to deal with that in your core business," he said. "And then you've got a whole new line of business — which is probably not a single line but multiple lines, because you don't know what's going to work. And you can't just walk away from your incumbent business, partly because you've got a lot of skills in that incumbent business that are helpful ... as [employees] put their toe — or maybe up to their ankle — into that new industry."

I agree — and I love seeing the leaders I interviewed doing all of this and so much more.

The greatest challenge of executing your real decarbonization strategy elements will be the imperative to balance today's operational and financial requirements with investing in new arenas. This balancing act will be reflected in every element of execution discussed in this book. And throughout each company's unique approach, there are likely to be several imperatives:

Explicitly articulate the balance. In 2022, the United Kingdom passed a windfall profit tax on oil and gas companies that (1) had barely made any money in the preceding years, and (2) were making significant investment in the energy transition with their newly returned profits. This indicated a failure on the part of policymakers (arguably reflecting the public's perception!) to understand why oil and gas profits are critical to energy transition activities. In both internal and external narratives of your real decarbonization strategy, it's important that you explain how you are able to invest in new areas (from profitable historic business lines) and why new business areas cannot be instantly profitable.

Tie in to the change story. The way a company narrates its transition strategy informs the way external and internal stakeholders assess its authenticity, its likelihood of success, and their willingness to support the effort. We will explore the power of the change story in Chapter 9.

Incorporate reporting and accountability. Investors, employees, and stakeholders will be looking for proof points in how companies execute their real decarbonization strategies. Therefore, it's extremely important that your reporting throughout the effort — including quarterly analyst calls, ESG reporting, and stakeholder presentations — return to your company's change story and how it balances the past and present. When you convey the roles of both old and new business lines in successes, failures, and course corrections, it shows that you have a steady hand in transition leadership.

An Uncertain but Highly Probably Future

The organizational structure you adopt for your real decarbonization strategy will reflect the unique opportunities your company will face. One thing is certain: What got your company to where it is today will not take it forward in this "uncertain but highly probably future." Shantanu Agarwal of Susteon stressed the central role of diversity in building successful teams for disruptive times. "A small, homogenous team may deliver on a small objective quickly," he told me, "but when you're talking about long, arduous, and difficult problems with lots of heterogeneity, diverse teams are always better."

Building out the organizational structure is where a lot of company leaders are comfortable. Move some boxes, draw some new lines, and voilà! In the case of your real decarbonization strategy, the structure must flow from your baseline, course, and people planning. This strategy requires a new frame of mind. To get there, ask yourself these questions:

- What does success with an empowered, bought-in workforce look like in my company?
- What systemic weaknesses does my new organization have to overcome?
- What will create connectivity between my company, team, and important internal and external stakeholder groups?
- How can I minimize our bureaucracy and maximize empowerment with appropriate accountability?
- Where can I create flexibility for fast failure and quick pivots?
- What silos will we risk forming through this process?
- In what way might I accidentally create haves and have-nots?
- Where are opportunities to balance accountability with freedom?

Then build out the structure, laying out clearly:

- The commitment of the board of directors
- Connectivity with and oversight of the board
- Senior leadership roles and responsibilities
- New and revised divisions, teams, or roles
- Resources and decision-making authority

Many leaders I interviewed think about the "uncertain but highly probably future" in the context of repurposing existing natural gas infrastructure for zero-carbon gases. "There's an opportunity for us to reduce our Scope 3 emissions, because natural gas is amazing in the fact that it can actually be transformed into a zero-carbon solution," Toby Rice of EQT told me. "And we can do that by transforming it into blue hydrogen and blue ammonia. And so we have a new ventures group here at EQT that is designed to invest in trying to find these cheap, reliable, zero-carbon solutions." Your company structure that supports real decarbonization will be designed to ensure that both today's natural gas infrastructure and your company are fit-for-purpose for future operations.

CHAPTER 8

Critical Element 4: Investment and Innovation

"Capital allocation is the most important thing that we do, because what we do today impacts us for decades to come."

— Vicki Hollub, Occidental

As you know from Chapter 1, David Victor of UCSD told me he was skeptical of oil and gas companies' ability to innovate at the speed and scale required to adapt to the energy future. Victor wasn't providing a critique of the sector, just his assessment. "The nature of the risk and the return in most of the energy transition technologies and businesses is totally different from the nature of risk and return in the conventional upstream oil and gas place," he said to me. Companies are, of course, investing and innovating. The key is that they aren't doing it in the same old way.

As an outsider, Victor astutely described what I heard from insiders. As he put it: "One thing that's very different — that's very unfamiliar — is managing the nature of risk and return, and it's unfamiliar not only for the company but for the shareholders." The piece I learned through my interviews, however, is that company leaders are embracing these differences. Take, for example, Oxy's demonstration of its direct air capture facility, which we will look at in a bit.

Publicly traded companies in particular have a lot to manage. By its nature, real decarbonization planning is long term in nature. Yet public companies are under the pressure of a quarterly review cycle to demonstrate results and explain their actions to shareholders. This need is compounded by the societal expectations that oil and gas companies transition immediately!

Paula Gant of GTI conveyed to me how she thinks of investments and innovation as part of a system: "This systems approach to innovation requires distributing strategic insights, invention, design, and creativity across the organization at all levels." In practice, this effort extends "beyond technology and into managerial innovation — building the skill, process, activities, and culture needed to unleash the potential of every person in the organization."

Developing a compelling strategy for investment and innovation is one way to channel investor, employee, and stakeholder expectations into a coherent narrative about the direction of the company, its values, and its contribution to civil society. Like all strategy components, it must be adapted to the company's starting point, available resources, time horizon, risk calculus, and culture. This chapter breaks down the steps that company leaders can take toward its creation.

Step 1: Determine the Objectives

It was a bit painful to hear (even though I had observed it myself) what Scott Sheffield of Pioneer had to say about investor reactions to ESG performance: "If you allocate more capital to ESG, then you won't see it in your stock performance at this time," he told me flatly. Sheffield, though, has his eye on a different prize: "Regardless, make sure you're doing the right thing and producing a low-carbon future for [investors]." The important thing is to determine your objectives — they will guide your real decarbonization strategy's investment and innovation.

My interviewees were unequivocal: Your investment strategy must be closely tied to your strategic vision and capital allocation plans. Real decarbonization does not work as a side hustle. Your real decarbonization investments will have to be directly tied to creating shareholder value on a meaningful time horizon. For example, Chad Zamarin explained Williams's objectives around its New Energy Ventures business this way: "We started looking at how we think things will be valued in 2030. The returns in which we invest today must translate into the business that we want in 2030. How will our shareholders view the value of those investments in 2030?"

I strongly recommend exploring the following themes to help determine the objectives of your real decarbonization investment strategy:

- What decarbonization course have you set (Chapter 4), and how does it inform your investment objectives?
- Over what time frame do you need to demonstrate progress? Emissions reduction results? Financial returns?
- Will you explore new frontiers, or do you need to stay close to your core business?
- Can your company go it alone, or do you need to collaborate with other companies?
- What is your risk-versus-reward tolerance?
- How will your stakeholders view failure?

With these inputs, you can lay out the objectives for your company.

Step 2: Evaluate the Options

There's a nearly infinite palette of potential investments in the energy transition. Vicki Hollub of Oxy told me she weighs these investments carefully. "Capital allocation is the most important thing that we do. Because what we do today impacts us for decades to come," she said. "Decisions have to be made very thoughtfully, and they have to be made with a focus on ensuring that we deliver returns and deliver value."

The range of opportunities for real decarbonization investment and innovation can be boiled down into the following arenas:

- Investment in pure science or technology R&D through such means as university partnerships and consortia
- Direct investment in start-ups, from seed funding to scaling
- Investment in new technologies and companies through partners such as incubators and venture capital firms
- Collaborations with companies, academia, and eNGOs such as the Oil and Gas Climate Initiative
- Investment in pilot and demonstration projects with start-ups and consortia

Technology investment is, of course, a common theme in a real decarbonization strategy. In our interview, Rob Sadler of DCP Midstream explained how a typical real decarbonization leader thinks about technological innovation: "We think it is critically important that we leverage technology and third-party companies to explore things that we can't even envision today." Sadler told me how DCP Midstream has seen marginal innovations in digitalization, for example, get better and better until they are economically viable. DCP Midstream likes to partner with venture capital firms so that those firms bring the company ideas to evaluate in pilot or field-scale programs. The approach both limits his company's risk and lets it get a first look at the technology.

Step 3: Dedicate the Resources

For companies just getting started, there is a chicken-and-egg dance: choosing whether to identify the financial and personnel resources to invest or to evaluate the opportunities themselves first. What has become clear to me from watching this awkward dance?

Companies *must* set aside specific dollar and personnel resources first. Hello, chickee!

You will need to iterate your innovation targets, needed resources, and dedicated personnel. As projects are selected and collaborations unfold, the allocated resources are never exactly the right match for the selected investments. Here's where you should start to ensure that you understand the investment landscape and can consider the right opportunities:

- Set aside a multi-year investment dollar amount with target spends for each year, for a minimum of three years.
- Designate an individual leader and team to explore, identify, and make recommendations for upcoming investments.

If you skip these two steps, two consequences will invariably emerge: (1) Your company will be unaware of many opportunities that exist, and (2) no one on your staff will bear responsibility for seeking out, evaluating, and following through on opportunities.

In the last decade I've had clients participate in dozens of innovation investments and collaborations, and the biggest upfront challenge is ensuring that the best opportunities get vetted. In the absence of a team with a vetting mission, many opportunities disappear, landing on the wrong person's desk or another cul-de-sac of company bureaucracy. Others never get into the organization at all, because the outside innovator can't figure out how to break through its many vendor firewalls. As a result, the company's innovation strategy is at the mercy of the vagaries of pet projects, insider connections, and company turf wars.

Yes, there is a lot of crap out there. Yes, there are infinite start-ups wanting your time, expertise, and money. Yes, there are too many industry consortia to fund, going in too many directions. So in the absence of a dedicated team with known investment resources, your exposure and selection will be haphazard at best. Dedicate a team, give it some money, and hold it accountable for making good choices.

Step 4: Set the Direction of Travel and the Guardrails

The infinite palette of investment opportunities must be narrowed right away, with strong company direction. Alan Armstrong of Williams, for example, told me that he directs that new investments must build on a "serious competitive advantage." He suggested investments in collaborations that can give the company a seat with a view to technology development. He wants to know what the future might look like, so it can inform the company's strategic plans.

Hollub described to me the profile of the firm Oxy wanted to select as contractor to build direct air capture plants. Oxy, she said, couldn't work with a firm focused on short-term profit or select one based on price alone. Her direction of travel: "It's going to take people who can look beyond that first-generation plant, or the second generation, and look to where we have to be, how soon can we get there, and what's it going to take to make it happen. Those companies that are innovative and committed are the ones we want to work with."

Once the direction of travel is clear, lay out the guardrails. Clear guardrails will help your team charged with identifying and evaluating investments narrow the range of possibilities before it begins the hard work of evaluating them. Examples of useful guardrails include guidance on

- Expectations to enhance the efficiency or reach of a specified core business
- Clear, definable connections to future business opportunities, within a certain level of certainty
- An articulated timeline for expected results, including a definition of what "results" may mean
- Rules of thumb for risk and return
- Out-of-bounds arenas, such as "no direct investment in start-up companies"
- Preferred types of investments, such as direct investment in joint ventures or group participation with peer companies

Together, the direction of travel and guardrails will provide a framework for the initial screening of opportunities, helping your team quickly set aside the lion's share of possibilities so they can home in on specific ideas for evaluation. Initially both the direction of travel and guardrails should be loosely defined. The team charged with innovation may find them either overly broad or unnecessarily restrictive and should be empowered to work with leadership to refine the framework.

Step 5: Articulate the Decision-Making Framework

The direction of travel and guardrails will be refined into decision-making criteria once a suite of investment opportunities has been identified. With a first batch of investment options, the team should propose to your company's leadership specific criteria and a decision-making process, with the flexibility to consider the unique nature of each option. Contribution to a university consortium cannot be directly compared with an investment in an energy-transition incubator. The process and criteria should be adaptable enough to allow for thorough consideration of both.

The effort should be galvanizing to the team involved. Hollub described in our interview how Oxy likes to build ownership in new efforts. The key, she told me, is "communicating to our employees what we need to accomplish and empowering them. ... We help our employees understand what the challenges are ... and what we need to achieve. Then we stay out of the way and allow them to do what they do best, and that is to go solve the problem in a way that only they can do it."

Hollub described this as a company culture "where the employee base is informed, engaged, and empowered."

To enable robust and timely investment decision-making, you might choose to delegate the process to different teams according to the type of opportunity. Dominic Emery of bp, for instance, described different evaluation teams assigned on the basis of the scale and nature of the investment, such as oil and gas, renewables, electric vehicles, or venture investment. The usual investment criteria will apply — ensuring clear lines of delivery, accountability, strategic fit, returns expectations, and alignment within the capital allocation plan. Operational and safety risk considerations remain evergreen, and carbon emissions and sustainability aims are also critical criteria for all material investments. Financial authority should lie at different levels for different investment types — from the board of directors through subsets of the executives and then to the venture investment committee for smaller-scale opportunities.

Select one leader to provide consistent oversight across the decision-making effort. For each type of opportunity, identify three to five evaluators, at least one of whom has expertise in the area under exploration, another who has deep understanding of the company's strategic direction, and one familiar with the company's current operations. Determine the number of steps in the decision-making process, who makes recommendations, and who will make the final decisions. Consider the need for socialization with relevant business operations or approval from the board of directors.

Specify preliminary criteria for evaluation as part of the decision-making process. These criteria will require iteration as the process unfolds. People cannot reasonably evaluate new business areas, determine the decision criteria, and evaluate an array of novel options in one fell swoop! Instead, provide them with the initial criteria and process, as well as the flexibility to ensure that iteration can take place.

Dan Harple vividly described to me how new ideas get evaluated at Context Labs. "It's really simple," he said. "It's called 'Bring a ball, kick a ball, don't kick each other.'" Ideas are written down and evaluated without identification of the person who proposed them, he explained, so the group assesses the idea instead of the person behind it. The process, Harple argued, "creates ... an egalitarian culture that allows and encourages people to innovate and disrupt."

You will select projects, identify teams to develop them, and allocate resources. These teams will set their objectives and targets, then draft business plans to be executed.

Step 6: Identify Milestones for Evaluation and Course Corrections

"Executing on the energy transition vision means you have to be innovative and creative," Hollub explained, "but you also have to be flexible. Because where you think you will go and how you think you will get there might not work out." To address the disparity between intention and reality, set a cadence for your evaluation of each investment against the criteria under which it was selected. Having an intentional evaluation cadence sets you up to pivot early and efficiently, if necessary, to a better path. As Hollub put it to me: "As we have made course corrections, sometimes we wind up going down a path that we didn't expect to go. And sometimes we've turned a corner that we didn't expect to see."

By anticipating the need for course corrections, your execution team can stay proactive and nimble, rather than doubling down on poor investments. The evaluation cadence will vary and be dictated by each investment's business plan.

Companies will have a dedicated team of leaders who evaluate investments annually and make recommendations on those investments to the ultimate decision-making body, either the senior leadership team or the board. The evaluation process of individual investments can then be used to refine the direction of travel, guardrails, and decision-making process. Each success or failure provides the experience required to improve the next year's investments. In this way, your real decarbonization investments can be integrated into many of your existing evaluation and decision-making processes.

To Announce or Not to Announce

There will be failures, mixed-bag results, and wild successes. Companies I work with have different approaches to making things public. Traditionally, oil and gas companies like to do all their innovation work in a subterranean fashion. They want to experiment, work out all the kinks, and then make announcements when they can explain every step and be as certain as possible of success.

But the evolving expectations around energy transition work have dramatically changed this calculus. Once companies started making aspirational emissions reductions commitments, all clear criteria for what to share publicly went out the window.

The pendulum on aspirational commitments probably went too far, and companies today need a disciplined approach to making announcements. Stakeholders want to see real action behind real decarbonization strategies; on the other hand, shareholders want to observe a methodical and calculated approach to making investments. You will therefore need to have a mix of (1) subterranean investments, which the company holds close while assessing their potential (or protecting trade secrets), and (2) a suite of very public, sometimes aspirational investments in collaborations, longer-time-horizon ventures, or expected successes.

What Are We Doing Here?

> *"Performing while transforming is the essence of what bp is doing. You cannot have one without the other."*
>
> — Dominic Emery, bp

Your company's real decarbonization strategy is deeply interwoven with people: complex, interesting people with their own histories, biases, and baggage. These people are your team, your partners, your investors, your stakeholders, your critics, and your family. And this work is hard — really, really hard.

So you need a strong story to reach through and allow these people to connect to your strategy.

You need a change story.

Your Change Story

Dominic Emery reflected on lessons learned from bp's early and ambitious foray into its energy evolution. One key takeaway: "We could have made our story clearer for our stakeholders — particularly our investors. This has now been done, based on recent investor commentary," he said.

Your company's change story needs to do five things:

Connect with and honor your company's past. For Williams, the story starts with the company's 100-year history. For Xcel Energy, it begins with the many generations of employees who created the foundation for the company's work today. For younger companies, such as EQT, it honors the legacy of the generations of companies and workers who came before. Grounding your change story in your company's history embraces your legacy employees and enterprises as foundational to the work ahead — and also provides a reality check on the scope and scale of company resources. Vicki Hollub of Oxy includes employees and their drivers in her change story. "What we're doing now with the energy transition is such a positive thing for all of our employees," she told me. "They recognize that we need to provide oil and gas to the world. We need to provide it in a better way than we've done in the past. And we need to do things differently so that we can eliminate the footprint of carbon for ourselves and for others. That is motivating to our employees."

Articulate the relationship between existing businesses and new ventures. DCP Midstream considers enhancing digitalization and operational efficiency core to both existing operations and energy transition efforts. Exxon is translating downhole expertise to carbon capture and sequestration. Maynard Holt connects the old and new in the way Veriten approaches challenges. When I asked him how his team pivoted from oil and gas expertise to all energy, he said: "There's a curiosity to the place, and there's always an element of going toward the new new thing. Because we have an energy bloodhound DNA, we end up looking like the world, because we're constantly following the world."

Clearly convey what is aspirational and what is concrete. When I convened an exploratory collaboration between a large oil and gas company and a pragmatic eNGO, the eNGO executive emphasized that now is the time to move beyond aspirational efforts. He said he considers an oil and gas company serious when it is ready to put

$50 million of steel in the ground. The change story *can* articulate what is aspirational, such as when Xcel Energy made the first utility net-zero commitment in 2018. Xcel conveyed clearly that the technology to meet the commitments didn't yet exist, but Xcel was sending a signal to the market. Your change story must quickly follow suit, detailing how the company is setting aside dedicated resources and dollars.

Clear the way for missteps and course corrections. There needs to be room for your new risk-reward calculus in your change story. As Hollub put it: "We have a strategy to, first, prove up our technologies. And as we prove up our technologies, we will look at alternative ways to finance the advancement of the infrastructure that we need to deliver the CO_2 and extract the CO_2. ... It's going to take not only the innovation but the flexibility to change course when we need to." Ensure that you are talking upfront, as Hollub does, about how you expect to make changes along the way.

Inspire optimism in the future. Above all, the change story lets investors, customers, employees, and communities know that their company is going to contribute to a brighter future. As one leader explained, "A change story can articulate a mid- to long-term North Star for the organization that articulates why things will be different and better in the future, which can help sustain colleague and investor confidence through the inevitable bumps along the way."

Rollout and Communications

Your real decarbonization strategy is fundamentally by and for people. Central to its success is conveying your change story to them. But the change story alone isn't enough: The strategy rollout and ongoing communications around the strategy are fundamental to ultimate success. The communications around your strategy both inform and reflect the strategy, from inception through introduction to your inevitable success. (I believe in you!)

After you mosey to the end of this book, you'll soon be heading back up to Chapter 3 to get started. Consider the following ideas to build communications into your efforts:

Socialization internally and externally. A listening tour, a working draft, a series of meetings to socialize these ideas — these are all ways that your leadership team can gather feedback on the plan. This important step will highlight your plan's weaknesses, air the inevitable critiques, and provide fertile ground for improvements on your ideas.

Incorporating feedback. Plan to spend months sharing the plan internally and externally. Set aside time and resources to revise your plans with the feedback you receive.

Announcements. Once your real decarbonization strategy is revised post-socialization, phase in appropriate announcements over time to ensure your team has the opportunity to under-promise on the strategy and over-deliver on its implementation. Consider these announcements an ongoing part of your strategy execution, paralleling your review-and-revise efforts.

Transparency and reporting. In keeping with company operations and ESG reporting, maintain a high degree of transparency in your recordkeeping, assessments, and course corrections. No one expects your energy strategy efforts to go perfectly. Everyone expects you to do what you said you would.

Throughout all your communications, keep returning to your change story. It can evolve to reflect your lessons learned and growth. Connect the pieces of your strategy to your most important audience — the people who will make it happen as employees, investors, community members, critics, and customers.

CHAPTER 10

The View from 2035

"You can't go back
and change the
beginning, but you
can start where
you are and change
the ending."

— C.S. Lewis

2035 is both a lifetime away and — for those of us who've been around for a little while — within the blink of any eye. In energy infrastructure terms, it's practically tomorrow. So here is our change story for the near future: Success in 2035 requires that today's oil and gas industry be central to an expanded, cleaner, affordable, reliable, and secure global energy system. Global carbon emissions will be falling (and U.S. emissions per capita will continue to fall). People around the world will continue to be brought into the middle class. Energy supplies to allies will be ensured.

Central to these worldwide economic and energy successes will be the fact that we are welcomed as energy innovators and leaders. We will be valued and trusted as civic-minded solution providers. Our success will fill the chasm currently separating energy reality and unrealistic expectations. Our achievements and influence will be limited only by the time it takes for us to leave the polarized fight in the past.

Success in 2035 for today's oil and gas executives requires that we care more about our legacy than our quarter-to-quarter success. Even millennial leaders today will have Gen Z nipping at their heels in 2035. We need to provide the energy leaders of 2035 with an energy system that they can be proud of.

My intention in writing this book was to provide oil and gas leaders with a guide for how to get to work on real decarbonization — without confusion or ambiguity. Here's what I learned in writing it: The biggest challenge of the energy future does not lie in the technology and innovation required. It's not in achieving the massive scale at which unprecedented building and reorganization must occur. And it's not even in the challenge of bringing 1 billion people globally out of poverty—because we know how to do that. It's our willingness to step into the breach and lead, to defy the stakeholders who don't want us to participate, to each build our own part of the global real decarbonization strategy.

So in 2035 others will gauge our success by three measures:

The ways in which we will put people at the center of our strategy. At its heart, the energy transition requires the buy-in of lots of people. No one is a spectator in the energy transition. The success of your real decarbonization strategy will require putting at its heart engagement, education, consideration, and participation — because that's how you get buy-in for the many tradeoffs required.

Within our companies, we will know our success by the extent to which we will have prepared our workforce for the changes that will occur. As Wouter van Kempen of DCP Midstream told me: "As you think about change, make sure you think about the culture of change — then you are thinking about the people part of change. It is our people who drive results and deliver through change." The authentic inclusivity of our diverse workplaces will ensure that we have the bench strength in leaders ready to take on the next chapter.

In success, our companies will be interwoven with the communities within which we will continue to build and operate, as co-creators of jobs, prosperity, good health, and clean surroundings. As Shantanu Agarwal of Susteon said in our interview, "Gen Z workers want to find a company that aligns with their mission." Our companies will play a clear, vital civic role. As a result, we will build partnerships with elected officials, policymakers, and regulators charged with the energy transition at every level of government. Alan Armstrong of Williams put it this way: "If you think about what it will take to be successful on projects, it is the political solutions that will distinguish us."

The resilience of our business model during political pendulum swings and technology innovation. Oil and gas engineers are the rocket scientists of the subsurface! In our evolution, we will no longer be considered part of a political identity, nor our products fuels of the past. Instead, we will have proven the responsiveness of our operations to changing consumer and customer expectations. As Toby Rice of EQT put it, celebrating our achievements: "This industry has created better technology than NASA, arguably, and we are the only industry that's proven we can thrive through massive transformation. Our industry can carry the weight of the world."

David Victor of UCSD told me he sees a world coming where a virtuous cycle of policy and innovation for real decarbonization keeps building on itself. In the beginning, he said, energy transition start-ups were "small companies run by dudes living in Berkeley, wearing Birkenstocks and smoking dope. And now that's still going on, but the industries are much bigger, much more powerful, and much better organized." As a result, Victor predicted "an evolution of policy that's much faster in the direction of an energy transition, because the political voice in favor of that gets stronger much more rapidly." In 2035, success will look like an energy industry constructively engaged in the virtuous cycle of policy that further supports an accelerated transition.

The contributions we will have made to the decarbonization of the energy system, the affordability of energy, the reduction of our

environmental footprint, and the reliability of energy delivery. One of the things I love about Matt Kolesar of Exxon is his optimism—and when it comes to 2035, he is optimistic about many things. For instance, he told me that "on a tactical level, methane and flaring should not be a thing anymore for oil and gas; we will have it almost completely addressed." And because renewables, hydrogen, expanded electrical infrastructure, and nuclear will be able to accomplish only so much between now and 2035, Kolesar believes that "large-scale decarbonized projects should be mainstream. Ideally, there will be CCS facilities associated with every large industrial complex in the world." Like me, Kolesar believes that "the significant progress that has been made on decarbonization will make policy discussions more civil" because "we'll have line of sight as a society of what decarbonization looks like." Real decarbonization, hitting the mainstream.

In 2035, the foundation will be in place for a zero-carbon system. As Victor described it, we will have "a heavy-industry-oriented hydrogen play" as well as an expanded electricity system, resulting in "two energy carriers, in effect, of the energy system of the future." The novel interplay between these systems will support renewables as well as create redundancy and therefore stability. As Victor sees it, "there could be a huge upside at that interplay. But is that upside going to be organized by the companies that are in the oil and gas business today, or new businesses of the future?" My answer: In 2035, today's oil and gas companies will be positioned with the scale to accelerate these transitions.

And so we end where we began—with my query to Victor: Can today's oil and gas companies lead into the energy future? My answer: Of course they can! Even Victor, ever the pragmatic skeptic, told me this: "Places that are on the front lines are spending a lot of their own money pioneering new technologies. And companies that want to watch what the future might be probably need to do a better job of watching what the pioneers are doing, not just to [see] when they fail, but to pay attention. And that's a little bit of fast following." Yes! Shall we call it aggressive, mindful, optimistic fast following?!

"But it has much deeper implications," Victor added. "Where the success stories are happening, you need to really be in the middle of that if you're going to be in the middle of the transition." Amen! That's why you are writing your real decarbonization strategy: to be square in the middle of everything happening in 2035.

There are others who will map success in 2035 to tons of CO_2 removed from the energy system and atmosphere, miles of zero-carbon infrastructure deployed, people raised out of energy poverty, and megawatts of clean energy delivered. I'm going to measure 2035 success by the ways in which we will have overcome a seemingly insurmountable obstacle: skepticism about our role and right to lead into the energy future. We will succeed in this leadership endeavor by taking our responsibility to lead wholeheartedly. Giddy up! As Mark Twain said: "Plan for the future, because that is where you are going to spend the rest of your life."

ACKNOWLEDGMENTS

Thank you to the awesome leaders who agreed to be interviewed for this book, both the unnamed and the named: Shantanu Agarwal, Alan Armstrong, Mark Brownstein, Paula Gant, Martha Hall Findlay, Dan Harple, Maynard Holt, Vicki Hollub, Alice Jackson, Matt Kolesar, Granville Martin, Anthony Oni, Toby Rice, Rob Sadler, Brian Schettler, Scott Sheffield, Wouter van Kempen, David Victor, and Chad Zamarin.

Thank you to Adán Rubio and Lindsey Slaughter for all their work getting the book to the page. My deep gratitude to the Adamantine team who do all the research and work that guides my thinking. Caroline Schweiter, I learn from you every edit! Thank you for your thoughtful, detailed work. (Who knew editing could be fun?!) Thanks to Anne Carto, who is always ready to support my crazy dreams ("You're writing another book? Already? Seriously? Okay, what do you need to make it happen?"). Anne reviewed the book in the final weeks before her wedding; now that's dedication. Thanks to Joe Evers, who reviewed *Real Decarbonization* while on a river trip in the Grand Canyon; I find that incredibly auspicious! Cover art and book layout by Rachel Valliere brought it all together. And special thanks to Bob Lalasz, who — every once in a while — dances on a table to get me to write a book. May there be many more dances.

Thanks to my husband, Brian, who suppresses a grin every time I pair "take it easy" with some new project, like this book. Brian is my everything. And pretty fun to hang out with! To my kiddos, Alec and Carter, thanks for inspiring me to be my best self — and for encouraging me relentlessly. I hope this work lives up to my potential.

And thank you, readers, for going out there and putting real decarbonization into practice, fulfilling our destiny to wholeheartedly lead into the energy future.

ABOUT THE AUTHOR

Tisha Schuller founded Adamantine Energy to provide thought leadership to future-proof energy businesses against rising social risk. Tisha advises private clients from Fortune 100 energy companies to nonprofit environmental organizations in matters including managing disruption, energy policy, business strategy, politics, and community engagement. She also serves as the strategic advisor for Stanford University's Natural Gas Initiative. Previously, Tisha served as president and CEO of the Colorado Oil & Gas Association and as principal and vice president of Tetra Tech, a national environmental consulting and engineering firm. She has a bachelor of science from Stanford University.

Tisha serves on many academic and nonprofit boards including those of the Breakthrough Institute, the Energy for Growth Hub, the Denver Museum of Nature & Science Institute for Science & Policy Strategic Council, the University of Wisconsin–Madison Nelson Institute for Environmental Studies, and the Payne Institute for Public Policy at the Colorado School of Mines, and she is a member of the National Petroleum Council, an advisory board to the U.S. secretary of energy under the Obama, Trump, and Biden administrations. Tisha's book *Accidentally Adamant* was published in 2018, and *The Gamechanger's Playbook: How Oil & Gas Leaders Thrive in an Era of Continuous Disruption* was published in 2020. Tisha writes a weekly series titled *Both of These Things Are True* and hosts the *Real Decarbonization* podcast.

Tisha lives in the mountains of Colorado in an old log cabin with her husband, Brian, and son Alec. Occasionally son Carter returns from college in Montana, to much celebration. The Schullers are surrounded by a huge extended clan, which gathers often and brings them much joy. Tisha and family enjoy trail running, fly fishing, hiking, and abundant high school hockey. Family pup Pearl and kitty Bella did everything in their power to interrupt the writing of this book.

Made in United States
North Haven, CT
13 March 2023

33990983R00070